Steve Parish

Amazing Facts about Australia's
Deadly&Dangerous
Wildlife

Text: Greg Czechura, Queensland Museum

Photography: Steve Parish

Contents

Australia's amazing
dangerous animals

Australia's amazing wildlife includes an astonishing array of beautiful and unusual creatures found nowhere else on Earth. Among them are some of the deadliest and most dangerous animals known to humans. There are venomous snakes and spiders, poisonous sea jellies, stinging and biting insects, huge crocodiles and sharks and a few "cuddly" mammals that can inflict painful injuries. All have an important place in Australia's natural environment.

DEADLY AND DANGEROUS ANIMALS live on the land, in the water, along our seashores and some even live close by in our cities and towns. Fortunately, human encounters with these animals don't happen very often. The animals are often shy and secretive, or are found in places where people seldom venture. For most of us, driving a car is a much bigger risk.

When people think of "dangerous" animals, they usually think of wild creatures, but in the wrong situation any animal can be a threat. Livestock, such as cattle and horses, and even domestic pets, are all capable of causing illness, injury or death. Statistics show people are more likely to be bitten by a cat or dog than by a snake, possum or any other Australian native animal. It is also important to remember that an "attack" by a deadly or dangerous animal is often a natural defensive behaviour.

This book examines some of Australia's deadly and dangerous animals, the potential risks that they pose to people and the best ways to manage these risks.

Above right: Death adder (*Acanthophis* sp). *Below:* White Sharks (*Carcharodon carcharias*) are widespread predators in temperate waters worldwide.

Bull ants (*Myrmecia* spp.) are aggressive insects that sting and bite.

Estuarine Crocodiles (*Crocodylus porosus*) are a hazard for travellers in northern Australia.

Black Rats (*Rattus rattus*) are infamous as carriers of some of the worst diseases known to humans.

STEVE SWANSON

Precautions

Many animals regard humans as a threat simply because humans are hunters and potential predators.

ABOUT THIS BOOK

Australia is synonymous with deadly and dangerous animals. The country has gained a certain infamy as a place besieged by killer sharks, snakes and crocodiles. All too often Australia's deadly and dangerous creatures are sensationalised, preyed upon themselves by the popular media. A good shark story sells, but the truth behind such stories involves a complicated relationship between humans, animals and the habitats they share. This book seeks to dispel some of the myths about Australia's deadly and dangerous creatures by presenting facts that are not only informative, but compelling. Truth, after all, is a lot more interesting than fiction.

Some communal insects, like these paper wasps (*Polistes* sp.), can be extremely aggressive if disturbed.

Australia's deadly and dangerous animals come in all shapes and sizes and often the most dangerous creatures are the ones you encounter everyday — viruses and pollutants kill millions of people every year. Statistically speaking, the humble mosquito is infinitely more lethal than a fully grown Estuarine Crocodile.

This book examines creatures that exist largely in our thoughts (most people will never see a wild taipan in their life) and also those that pass unseen before our eyes every day (bacteria and various parasites).

We have divided this book into sections based on the danger posed by various animals and conditions (physically dangerous, venomous, poisonous, disease-carrying and environmental hazards). Precautions for avoiding danger are outlined on each spread, and a range of amazing facts are set out in side columns on each page.

the FACTS!

THE ANIMAL RESPONSIBLE for causing the most human deaths per year worldwide is *Homo sapiens* — the human being. For example, the death toll for World War II (Sept 1939–Aug 1945) was an estimated 72 million people — 26 million military personnel and 46 million civilians (including deaths due to war-related famine and disease).

NO ONE IS SURE WHY AUSTRALIA has so many deadly and dangerous animals. The country's warm climate may be a factor. Tropical and subtropical areas usually have a greater species diversity than more temperate regions. Some scientists believe it may be an accident of evolution or a response to a harsh environment.

ANY LARGE ANIMAL is potentially dangerous. Even those that are very tolerant of humans and regarded as "friendly" can cause injury and death in unusual circumstances. A surfer in Western Australia was attacked and badly bitten by an Australian Sea-lion (*Neophoca cinerea*). A woman was injured when she was struck by a leaping dolphin that landed in a small boat in New Zealand's Bay of Plenty. (The animal apparently did not see the boat before it made its leap.) Sea-lions and dolphins (left) normally pose little or no risk to humans.

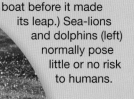

5

What is a
dangerous animal?

A "dangerous" animal is one that poses a threat to another animal, human beings included. Animals are considered dangerous for many reasons and not just because they bite or sting. The physical characteristics of an animal, its temperament and the circumstances in which it is encountered all affect how it will interact with people.

the FACTS!

WILD ANIMALS DO NOT ALWAYS REGARD HUMANS as an immediate threat and some may approach closely out of curiosity. In other circumstances, people have been injured or killed by wild animals because they have encountered an angry or scared animal that has been already attacked by another animal or person. People going to the "rescue" of their pets are often the victims of bites and stings that were not really intended for them.

MANY ANIMALS ARE ONLY "DANGEROUS" at certain times of the year, such as during the breeding season (when there is competition for mates), or during a particular stage in their life cycle (such as parasites). So little is known about some Australian animals that researchers are not sure whether they are dangerous or harmless.

TIGER SNAKE ANTIVENOM was released in 1930 after several years of research between the Commonwealth Serum Laboratories and the Walter and Eliza Hall Institute in Melbourne. It was the first antivenom developed in Australia and, since then, another 12 antivenoms have been developed for dangerous Australian snakes, fish, spiders and ticks.

IN THE PAST 500 YEARS, humans around the world have caused the extinction of almost 1000 animal species.

MICHAEL CERMAK

Many people mistakenly believe that only "ugly" animals, such as spiders and snakes, are dangerous. This is not true. Some dangerous animals (fish and cone shells) are very attractive in appearance.

ONE OF THE MOST SERIOUS THREATS comes from animals that regard humans as prey to be eaten. Fortunately, Australia does not have any large terrestrial predators like tigers or bears. The largest and most dangerous Australian predators are Estuarine Crocodiles and sharks, which do not distinguish between humans and any other sort of potential prey.

Danger is not always related to size. Protozoans are among the smallest living organisms, but they are capable of causing illness and death on a very large scale. Similarly, "cute and cuddly" animals are often considered harmless because of their attractive appearance, but this isn't always the case.

There are animals with venomous bites or poisonous stings and some that use chemicals to defend themselves. Others have sharp teeth, claws and spurs that can wound soft human skin. Then there are animals that carry disease organisms and parasites, which can affect our health and well-being.

PEOPLE ARE A PROBLEM TOO

Most deadly or dangerous animals do not attack people unless they are accidentally, or deliberately, provoked. Even then, frightened animals often perform a "threat display" to scare or intimidate the "aggressor" before they actually attack. Human beings often fail to recognise these warnings, or ignore them with disastrous results.

When threatened, the Frillneck Lizard (*Chlamydosaurus kingii*) raises its neck frill to frighten would-be predators.

Precautions

It should always be remembered that "wild" animals are exactly that — wild. They are not tame pets or toys and should always be treated with caution. A wild animal's reaction to a human being will always be unpredictable.

WHAT ARE THE RISKS?

Identifying "deadly and dangerous" animals is not always easy. Most people understand the risks associated with large crocodiles or venomous spiders because these animals are often found near humans and are known to cause serious injury and sometimes death.

Other animals may possess dangerous attributes, such as highly toxic venom, but rarely cause harm because they are not in frequent contact with humans. The Western Taipan (*Oxyuranus microlepidotus*) is one of the world's deadliest snakes, but it inhabits the remote Channel Country of far south-western Queensland and is seldom seen by people.

Normally placid or shy animals often become aggressive during the breeding season, when males are more likely to fight over territories or females. Human sensitivity to animal toxins is also an important factor and explains why bee or wasp stings can cause serious allergic reactions in some people and not others.

the FACTS!

A NEWLY DISCOVERED SPECIES of taipan from Central Australia (*Oxyuranus temporalis*) is known only from a single specimen and it has never been responsible for biting a human. However, given its close relationship to other taipans, it must be regarded as a potentially very dangerous species.

HONEY BEES, DOGS, CATTLE AND HORSES kill and injure more people annually than native wildlife.

THE AUSTRALIAN BUSH can be a very dangerous place, but its biggest danger is not its wildlife. Vehicle breakdown, remoteness, lack of water and extreme temperatures are far more hazardous for ill-prepared travellers. In northern Australia, wet season deluges can often strand travellers for weeks on end.

Animals that are in poor health (like these brumbies) and that are living close together in harsh and dirty conditions are very susceptible to the organisms that cause disease. Some animal diseases can be transmitted to humans.

APPROXIMATELY 120,000 DEATHS occur in Australia each year. Animal- or wildlife-related deaths do not appear among the 10 most common causes of death, which include motor vehicle accidents, suicide, assault, poisoning, drowning, burns, falls and medical complications.

HUMAN FATALITIES IN AUSTRALIA 1980–1990

Cause	Total deaths	Annual rate
Crocodile attacks	8	0.7
Shark attacks	11	1
Bee stings	19	1.7
Lightning strikes	20	1.8
Drowning	3455	345
Motor vehicle accidents	32772	2979

Visitors should observe the water safety warnings depicted below. Your co-operation will prevent tragedies from occurring.

No lifesaving service | Slippery rocks | Unexpected waves | Strong currents

Types of
dangerous animals

RON & VALERIE TAYLOR

Different sorts of animals pose different risks to humans. Deadly and dangerous animals can be grouped according to the type of harm they cause. Animals can be physically dangerous, poisonous, venomous and carriers of disease and parasites.

THE WORDS "POISON", "VENOM" AND "TOXIN " are often used interchangeably, but each has a different meaning.

Poisons are substances that cause damage, illness or death if they are absorbed by ingestion (eating) or contact (touching). Toxins are poisons produced by a plant or animal for defence or predation. Most toxins interfere with the body's biochemical processes and cells. Venoms are toxins produced by animals that possess a mechanism to directly transfer the venom to prey or aggressors via bites, stings, sprays and wounds.

Sea anemones are considered venomous because they have special cells called nematocysts that inject toxins into other animals. The risk for humans varies according to the species of anemone.

the FACTS!

THE PROCESS OF TRANSFERRING VENOM from one animal to another is called "envenomation".

THERE ARE ABOUT 3000 snake bites reported Australia-wide each year. Of these, 200–500 will require treatment with antivenom and, on average, only one or two deaths will occur. In the early 1900s, death rates were as high as 40–50% for death adder and tiger snake bites alone. The decline in the number of deaths from snake bite is due to the development of effective antivenoms (below) and improved medical treatment.

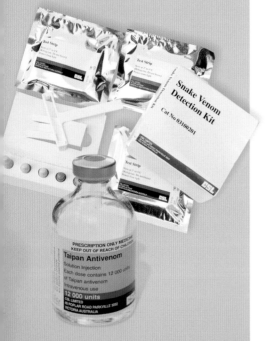

Snake Venom Detection Kit
Cat No 03100201

PRESCRIPTION ONLY MEDICINE
KEEP OUT OF REACH OF CHILDREN

Taipan Antivenom
Solution Injection
Each dose contains 12 000 units
of Taipan antivenom
Intravenous use

12 000 units
CSL LIMITED
45 POPLAR ROAD PARKVILLE 3052
VICTORIA AUSTRALIA

TOXIN ALERT!

Poisonous animals produce their own toxins or extract toxins from other sources (such as the food they eat). The toxins may be stored in an animal's skin, its body tissues or internal organs and can become more concentrated as the animal grows or ages. When a poisonous animal is attacked, the toxin is passed by ingestion or through skin contact. Frogs and toads often have poisonous skin secretions and some insects are able to store toxins in their bodies from the plants they eat.

The Cane Toad (*Bufo marinus*) is an introduced pest that is toxic at all stages of its life.

FAR LEFT: RON & VALERIE TAYLOR; CENTRE: IAN MORRIS

Precautions

If you do not recognise an animal, do not touch it. Some dangerous animals may resemble harmless species, but can only be identified by experts or scientific examination.

Butterfly cod or scorpionfish (*Pterois* and *Dendrochirus* spp.) have venomous spines.

In Australia's early days camels were invaluable to explorers and settlers, but they are known to be cantankerous animals and quick to bite.

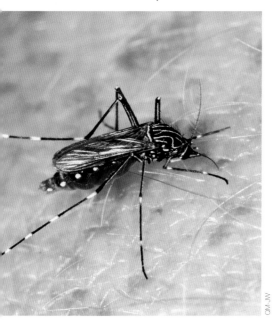

Mosquitoes are often considered to be the most dangerous animals on the planet because of the number of diseases they transmit to humans.

VENOMOUS ANIMALS

Venomous animals also produce their own toxins, but they are able to inject these toxins into other animals via stings, spines, sprays and fangs. Some animals, such as snakes and cone shells, have evolved venoms that not only disable their prey, but also start to break down the victim's body so that digestion is easier.

PHYSICALLY DANGEROUS

Any animal that is as big as or larger than a person can be dangerous, especially if it regards a human as an easy meal. Few Australian native animals are large enough to pose this sort of threat, but livestock, such as cattle and horses, have the size and weight to crush, trample and kill. Adult wild pigs can also be dangerous. Many animals have sharp claws and teeth, horns and tusks, piercing spines and blade-like projections, or hard beaks on their bodies. These animals can inflict deep wounds, punctures and severe lacerations in self-defence.

DISEASE-CARRYING ANIMALS

Compared to a human, a mosquito is a small, fragile creature, but some species are regarded as the deadliest animals on Earth. Mosquitoes carry parasites, bacteria and viruses that can cause life-threatening diseases such as Malaria, Japanese Encephalitis and Dengue Fever. Other types of insects are also known to transmit disease. Many other kinds of animals carry diseases and parasites that can affect humans. People can be directly infected through bites and scratches, or indirectly through excretions. Some particularly nasty diseases originate with our closest animal companions — domestic pets and livestock.

QM-JW

the FACTS!

TOXINS OFTEN TARGET A PARTICULAR PART of the victim. Neurotoxins affect the nervous system; cytotoxins attack the body cells; myotoxins damage muscles; and haemotoxins destroy blood cells and stop blood clotting.

THE COMPOSITION OF A VENOM is determined by the prey an animal eats. Venoms, such as those produced by snakes, are complex and contain many kinds of toxic substances.

BOTULISM IS A SEVERE TYPE OF FOOD poisoning caused by a microscopic bacteria (*Clostridium botulinum*). The bacteria lives on decaying matter and the toxin is one of the most poisonous natural substances in the world. Food that is not cooked, preserved or canned properly provides ideal conditions for the bacteria to grow. Botulism affects the nervous system and can also be fatal. Fortunately, outbreaks in the human population are rare.

ANIMAL POISONS AND VENOMS are now being used to develop new medicines. Venoms and poisons contain many different substances and scientists are finding that some of these may be useful for treating illnesses. For example, the venom of some scorpions contains substances that could help diabetes sufferers.

Sharks
— supreme predators

Sharks are considered the most terrifying of all marine creatures and shark attacks often appear brutal and violent. One species, the White Shark (Carcharodon carcharias), is feared above all others. The reality is that although some 40 shark species have been known to attack humans, only three species are to blame for most injuries and fatalities.

the FACTS!

THE SHAPE of a shark's teeth is influenced by its diet, ranging from needle-like teeth for gripping fish and flat teeth for crushing molluscs to triangular, serrated teeth for shearing flesh from marine mammals and large fish.

WHITE SHARKS have acute eyesight, hearing and sense of smell. They can also detect low-frequency vibrations and minute electric fields and they respond to taste and touch.

THE WHITE SHARK (below) is the only "warm-blooded" shark. All other sharks are cold-blooded. White Sharks are able to keep their body temperature higher than that of the surrounding water.

BULL SHARKS are able to move between saltwater and freshwater and have been found thousands of kilometres from the sea in the upper reaches of the Amazon River. Bull Sharks also inhabit Australian rivers and have been recorded up to 90 km inland from the mouth of the Brisbane River in Queensland.

ANY ANIMAL IS AT A DISADVANTAGE when it is out of its element and humans are no exception. Whether wading in the shallows, or swimming in deep water, humans are no match for powerful aquatic predators like sharks.

RON & VALERIE TAYLOR

The maximum size reached by White Sharks has been the source of many debates and wild speculation. Research indicates that the maximum total length is likely to be about 7 m.

RON & VALERIE TAYLOR

Sharks, like this whaler shark (*Carcharhinus* sp.), are sleek, active predators that are constantly on the move. In contrast, bottom-dwelling sharks have a body shape that is appropriate for a more stealthy life on the sea floor.

TOP OF THE FOOD CHAIN

Sharks are an evolutionary success story. They have been around for about 400 million years and "modern" sharks have existed almost unchanged for some 250 million years. The living species range from the harmless 15 m Whale Shark (*Rhincodon typus*) to the 15 cm Dwarf Lantern Shark (*Etmopterus perryi*).

Sharks eat almost anything, from plankton and other invertebrate animals to large fish, marine mammals and, if the opportunity arises, humans.

Precautions

Do not swim alone and avoid the water at night, dawn and dusk. Do not enter the water if sharks are present. Heed shark alarms, but do not panic. If attacked by a shark, try to hit the animal as hard as possible on the snout. The eyes and gills are also sensitive.

Physically dangerous

SHARK ATTACK

Despite their reputation, sharks are not a serious threat to human life. Worldwide, only about 100 attacks are recorded each year and in Australia the incidence of fatal shark attack is low — less than one fatality per year.

A human handling a shark is the main cause of attack. This occurs when people attempt to remove sharks from fishing nets or when they try to grab sharks or feed them. Most attacks occur in inshore waters when sharks are hunting. Attacks are also common near steep ocean drop-offs where prey congregates.

Sharks in a "feeding frenzy" should never be approached. They become excited when attacking schools of fish, when water oxygen levels are elevated or when there is blood in the water. It is possible that some shark attacks are opportunistic and may result from the shark mistaking swimmers and surfers for large prey animals.

Divers can be protected from the bites of small sharks by wearing coats of metal links or "chainmail".

THE BIG THREE

The White Shark, also known as the Great White or White Pointer, is thought to be responsible for nearly half of all the unprovoked fatal shark attacks on humans worldwide. It occurs in temperate to tropical waters around the world and research shows that White Sharks are very mobile, some even travelling across oceans.

The Tiger Shark (*Galeocerdo cuvier*) is named for the dark spots, blotches or bands across its back. It is smaller and slower than a White Shark and is found in temperate and tropical waters where it causes about 15% of unprovoked attacks.

The Bull Shark (*Carcharhinus leucas*) has an aggressive and unpredictable nature and is often found in rivers and canals. It is believed to be responsible for around 13% of unprovoked attacks worldwide and feeds on fish (including other sharks), dolphins, turtles, birds and other marine animals.

Below: The Tiger Shark has a reputation as an animal that will eat almost anything — it is a both a predator and a scavenger.

the FACTS!

MOST SHARK SPECIES are harmless and many are now under threat worldwide from fishing and habitat loss. More than 160 species of shark have been recorded in Australian waters.

SHARKS AND THEIR CLOSE RELATIVES, the rays, are "cartilaginous fish", which means that their skeletons are composed of light-weight, flexible cartilage.

SHARKS AND RAYS have tough skin studded with numerous, tooth-like scales known as "dermal denticles". The shape of the denticles varies among species and is a useful identification tool.

SHARK AND RAY SKIN can be made into leather (shagreen). The rough texture of shagreen makes it an ideal covering for sword grips.

SHARK TEETH are embedded in the flesh of their jaws and the outermost rows are constantly shed and replaced by "waves" of new teeth that form inside the jaws.

RON & VALERIE TAYLOR

11

Fish
— cuts & slashes

Some rays and bony fish (fish that have bony skeletons) can also inflict painful injuries on unsuspecting humans and a few species can even cause death. The same circumstances that provoke shark attack — close contact, attempted feeding or unusual circumstances — also apply to these animals.

the FACTS!

THE MANTA RAY (*Manta birostris*), the largest of the rays, may reach 7.6 m across its pectoral fins (or "wings") and can weigh up to 3000 kg. It is harmless.

NUMBFISH (OR NUMB RAYS) have electric organs on each pectoral fin. These are used to shock crabs, worms and fish. Once the prey is stunned, the numbfish expands its mouth and swallows its prey. Most numbfish bury themselves in sandy or muddy bottoms.

TORPEDO RAYS get their name from the Latin word *torpere*, which means "to be stiffened or paralysed". This refers to the consequences of handling or stepping on one of these rays.

MAKO SHARKS (*Isurus* spp.) are fast, aggressive fish that have been known to attack divers as well as damage boats and injure anglers after being hooked. They are regarded as one of the best and most dangerous of all gamefish.

BARRACUDAS OCCUR in tropical and some temperate waters (below). A typical barracuda is small-scaled, slender with two well-separated dorsal fins, a jutting lower jaw and a large mouth armed with large, sharp teeth. There are about 26 species of barracuda worldwide.

TIGERS OF THE SEA

Barracudas have been known to occasionally attack anglers, swimmers and divers, usually when the victims come between the fish and its prey, or when barracudas have been caught or speared. Barracudas are able to inflict lacerations and deep wounds with their sharp, jagged teeth and strong jaws. Barracudas are sometimes called the "tigers of the sea" because they are such ferocious hunters.

WATCH THE SPEAR!

Long Toms, alligator gars and needlefish are fast, surface-feeding predators that have long, thin pointed jaws and long, streamlined bodies. Long Toms often jump out of the water when alarmed or attracted to night lights. Like a spear, the sharp, bony snout of a Long Tom can cause death or serious injury if it punctures a person's head or torso.

RON & VALERIE TAYLOR

The Great Barracuda (*Sphyraena barracuda*) grows to 2 m in length and looks fierce. Apart from some occasional bites, this large fish does not pose a serious danger to humans.

NOT A HANDY SAW

Sawfish are rays that have a long, saw-toothed snout. When feeding, the "saw" is swung from side to side to impale and injure fish. It can also be used to disturb hidden prey and for defence. The sharp teeth along its edges can inflict deep lacerations.

ELECTRIC SHOCKS

Torpedo rays or "numbfish" use electrical discharges to capture prey and ward off aggressors. The shock is delivered by specialised organs that can deliver an 8–220 volt discharge. Anglers have been shocked when removing these rays from lines or nets. Other types of fish (including knife fish and catfish) can also generate electrical impulses.

Precautions

Take care in the water — look but don't touch. Do not feed large fish by hand and try not to disturb resting rays. Wear shoes even when wading in shallow water.

ANGLERS BE AWARE

Marlin, sailfish, spearfish and swordfish are known as "billfish" because of their long, rapier-like upper jaw or "bill". They are popular with anglers because of their speed, large size and fighting qualities, but anglers have suffered stab wounds to the body and have had limbs impaled as they hauled their catch aboard.

LOOK BUT DON'T FEED

Moray eels spend most of their time concealed inside crevices and alcoves in coral reefs. Morays have long, razor-sharp teeth and powerful jaws. Divers attempting to feed them have occasionally been bitten and attacks have resulted in muscle damage, chipped bones and the loss of fingers and limbs.

Right: Moray eels (*Gymnothorax* sp.)

A SURGEON'S SCALPEL

Many fish have protective spines on the body or fins, but the aptly named surgeonfish have razor-sharp bony blades or "scalpels" just in front of the tail fin. The scalpels normally lie flat, but stand erect when the fish is alarmed and can cut deeply if a fish is handled. Wounds from surgeonfish can remain painful for several days. Surgeonfish occur around most of Australia, except for cooler southern waters.

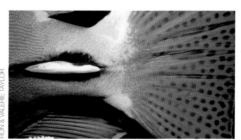

Above, left to right: A twin-bladed unicornfish (*Naso* sp.); A single-bladed surgeonfish (*Acanthurus* sp.). *Below:* Surgeonfish are brightly coloured or strikingly patterned inhabitants of Australia's coral and rocky reefs.

the FACTS!

THE QUEENSLAND GROPER (*Epinephelus lanceolatus*, below) grows to more than 2 m long and weighs more than 300 kg, making it one of the largest bony fish. In the past, gropers, which are found throughout the Indo-Pacific region, have been vilified as man-eaters. However, although some divers claim to have been butted or bitten while feeding them, gropers are not regarded as dangerous. They have also been know to grab shiny diving helmets.

TO PREVENT CONTACT and possible injury from moray eels, keep your hands out of rocky areas, holes and crevices when diving. Do not feed or tease morays by offering and withdrawing food. If you must, use a stick to probe. If you are fishing be careful, as dead fish, blood or bait will bring them out of their holes.

FISHING MAY BE THE MOST DANGEROUS SPORT in the world. More people have died from drowning, electrocution, accidents and disease due to fishing than most other sports combined. Statistically, however, the risk to any individual is low because of the huge number of people who fish.

Crocodiles
— ancient reptiles

Crocodiles are truly awesome animals. These low-slung, armoured reptiles have been the "top" predators in wetland and marine environments for millions of years. The "man-eaters" among them have long inspired terror among humans.

the FACTS!

CROCODILES EVOLVED from land-dwelling reptiles. Fossils of *Junggarsuchus sloani*, a slender, 1 m crocodilian from China, show that their ancestors had powerful jaws long before crocodiles returned to the water. The *Junggarsuchus* fossils are 230–150 million years old.

ABORIGINAL AND TORRES STRAIT ISLANDER peoples have a special relationship with crocodiles. Some groups regard crocodiles as religious icons or totems and others believe they are the spirits of creation ancestors. Crocodiles are also a food source for some Indigenous peoples, who take eggs from nests and hunt adults.

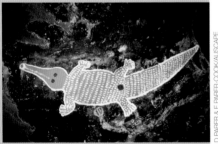

THE SEX OF ESTUARINE CROCODILES is determined by the incubation temperature in the nest. If the temperature is below 30 °C, females will hatch. Males will appear above 32 °C.

Male Estuarine Crocodiles over 5 m are rare (6.3 m is the maximum recorded). Females reach about 3 m. The heaviest crocodile known exceeded 1000 kg, but most weigh 400–500 kg.

LIKE SHARKS, crocodiles have a long evolutionary history. They have remained relatively unchanged over the past 80 million years. Their ancestors were land-dwelling predators that existed before the dinosaurs.

Tropical northern Australia is home to two species of crocodile — the Freshwater Crocodile (*Crocodylus johnstoni*) and the much larger Estuarine (or Saltwater) Crocodile (*Crocodylus porosus*).

Crocodiles have excellent underwater and night vision combined with a keen sense of smell. Small sensory buds around the top and bottom jaws allow crocodiles to detect vibrations — crucial when hunting in murky water. Their jaws have immense crushing power, enabling them to easily break skulls and other bones. Prey is swallowed as large chunks. If prey is too big to swallow whole, the crocodile may roll several times or shake its head in an attempt to break off a more manageable piece.

IMPRESSIVE HUNTERS

Estuarine Crocodiles are the largest living crocodile. They range from India to Vanuatu and the Solomon Islands. In tropical northern Australia, these crocodiles inhabit estuaries, rivers, swamps, beaches and offshore islands. They are sometimes seen basking on the banks of watercourses, or swimming or floating just below the water's surface. Crocodiles are skilful, stealthy predators. Most attacks occur at, or near, the water's edge. The muscular tail is used to power an attack, driving the animal forward or enabling it to lunge vertically with explosive force.

A large male Estuarine Crocodile is capable of taking an animal as large as a Water Buffalo (*Bubalus bubalis*), but most of its diet consists of crustaceans, fish, turtles, lizards, small mammals and birds.

Precautions

Never assume that crocodiles are not present just because they cannot be seen. Observe warning signs and be very careful around tropical creeks, rivers and lagoons.

Physically dangerous

THEY MAY BE SMALLER BUT...

The Freshwater Crocodile inhabits inland waterways and the tidal reaches of some rivers across northern Australia. It is smaller than the Estuarine Crocodile and has a long narrow snout, fine needle-like teeth and a row of four large scales on the neck immediately behind the head.

Freshwater Crocodiles are not normally regarded as dangerous but they can cause serious injuries if they do bite. These crocodiles are active during the day, although they mainly hunt at night. They ambush prey at the edges of rivers, creeks and lagoons, or in shallow water, catching insects, crustaceans, fish, frogs, lizards, turtles, bats and birds and sometimes small mammals.

IAN MORRIS

Male Freshwater Crocodiles weigh up to 60 kg and grow more than 2.5 m long. Females weigh up to 30 kg and reach 1.8 m.

STAYING SAFE

- Don't assume it's safe to swim just because there are no warning signs.
- Stay alert around waterways and lagoons and away from the water's edge.
- Don't return to the same place at the water's edge on a regular basis.
- Don't clean fish near the water or discard fish scraps in the water.
- If you see a crocodile slide mark (a crocodile moving into the water from a river bank will leave a characteristic mark), stay well clear of that area.
- Avoid places where native animals or cattle drink.
- Be particularly careful at night.

Right, top to bottom: Freshwater Crocodile; Estuarine Crocodile. Both species have attacked humans, though the Freshwater Crocodile is generally not considered dangerous.

RON & VALERIE TAYLOR

MICHAEL CERMAK

the FACTS!

FATAL ATTACKS by Estuarine Crocodiles are a rare occurrence in Australia. Victims of non-fatal attacks can be injured, not only by the bite, but also by blows from the tail. In high risk areas, always observe crocodile warning signs (below). On average, there is one fatal attack every two years.

CLARE THOMSON

STUDIES HAVE SHOWN that crocodiles are able to convert as much as 50–70% of their food into growth and energy (humans use only 3–4%). This means that crocodiles can go for months without eating.

IAN MORRIS

Turtles & lizards
— close combat

Australia is home to many fascinating reptiles, ranging from marine and freshwater turtles to lizards and snakes. Most reptiles are harmless and inoffensive but, like all animals, they will defend themselves if they are provoked or handled by humans.

A REPUTATION FOR BITING

Marine and freshwater turtles have jaws covered with plates that act like shears or scissors. All turtles will bite and the jaws of the larger marine species are strong enough to cut and crush fingers.

Feeding small freshwater turtles can also be risky. Short-necked, freshwater turtles (*Emydura* spp. and their relatives) have a reputation for biting and are often known as "snapping turtles". Large specimens of the genus *Elseya* and the Saw-shelled Turtle (*Wollumbinia latisternum*) are able to inflict deep wounds on careless hands.

Loggerhead Turtles have jaws that act like pinking shears for nipping off pieces of seagrass.

the FACTS!

SOME INDIGENOUS PEOPLES regard goannas as an important food source. Depictions of goannas often appear in traditional paintings (above).

SIX SPECIES OF MARINE TURTLE are found in Australia — the Green (*Chelonia mydas*), Hawksbill (*Eretmochelys imbricata*), Olive Ridley (*Lepidochelys olivacea*), Leatherback (*Dermochelys coriacea*), Loggerhead (*Caretta caretta*) and Flatback (*Natator depressus*). The survival of all is threatened by boat strikes, illegal and unmanaged fishing, habitat destruction, pollution and rising sea levels and temperatures.

BUSH FOLKLORE says that goanna bites never heal. This is not true, but the belief may have arisen due to infections caused by bites.

TOXIC SALIVA

Many lizards (and "harmless" snakes) have toxic saliva, but lack the means to inject it. Only two lizards (*Heloderma* spp.), which are found in the Americas, are truly venomous. Any large lizard will bite and scratch if carelessly handled. The large goannas (*Varanus* spp.) are also scavengers, so their teeth and claws may harbour infectious bacteria. The largest lizards will use their tail to lash out at an aggressor. The Perentie (*Varanus giganteus*), Australia's largest lizard, is capable of delivering a blow with sufficient force to unbalance a person.

Left: **Yellow-spotted Monitor (*Varanus panoptes*)**

QM-GC

Pythons
— a tight squeeze

Precautions

All reptiles will bite if handled or provoked. Large reptiles can inflict painful bites, cuts and scratches. Look but do not touch.

Physically dangerous

Australia is home to some of the world's most venomous snakes (see pages 44–49), but it also has many "harmless" species, including tree snakes and fourteen species of python. "Harmless" snakes will bite, but they are incapable of injecting venom or toxic saliva.

PYTHONS, AND THEIR RELATIVES

the boas, are often called "constrictors" because they kill by coiling their body tightly around prey. The prey is not crushed, but dies from suffocation and stress. A mature python is powerful enough to subdue a much larger animal. For example, Carpet Pythons (*Morelia spilota*) have been known to capture and kill small wallabies and adult Koalas (*Phascolarctos cinereus*).

On rare occasions, large constrictors in Asia have allegedly killed people. This does not happen as frequently as the media claims and the details surrounding such deaths are usually not known. Many reports are untrue. More often, owners of large captive pythons have been strangled or smothered while handling their pets without assistance. In these circumstances, the handler has usually lost control of a heavy snake, which then coils around the person's neck.

Left: The rainforests of Cape York Peninsula are the home of the Green Tree Python (*Morelia viridis*). This species is so rarely encountered that most Australians will never see one in the wild.

the FACTS!

SNAKES HAVE MANY MORE TEETH than mammals. Some snake species have more than 200 teeth.

SNAKE TEETH are usually all the same length and size, except for the elongated front teeth of boas and pythons and the fangs of venomous snakes. Snake teeth are attached to the side of the jawbone and are shed regularly. Shedding ensures the teeth remain sharp and are quickly replaced if damaged.

CARPET PYTHONS (below) occur across northern, eastern and south-western parts of mainland Australia. Colour pattern varies greatly between individuals.

PYTHONS LOCATE WARM-BLOODED PREY by means of heat-sensory pits located along the lower jaw. The pits can detect temperature changes of less than one-thirtieth of a degree.

CARPET PYTHONS often take up residence in roof and wall spaces in houses. Although they may occasionally frighten the home-owner, it should be remembered that they help control rats and mice!

RELUCTANT BITERS

Contrary to popular belief, most snakes are reluctant biters. If threatened, they will attempt to hide, flee, or bluff the attacker into leaving them alone. They will even emit offensive odours to keep an attacker at bay.

Bites by large pythons are likely to result in deep tears. This is because snake teeth curve backward and are designed to grip prey. If a large snake is pulled from a bite site, tearing and opening of the wound is likely. In addition, some teeth may be dislodged, increasing the risk of secondary infection.

The most common and familiar Australian python is the Carpet Python. This snake can be unpredictable. Some are very placid, while others are very easily aroused if they are approached.

Black Swan (*Cygnus atratus*)

Birds
— feathered furies

Unpleasant encounters with birds are most likely to occur when people handle or get too close to wild birds or their nests. Sharp beaks, claws and sometimes wings are a bird's main defensive weapons.

the FACTS!

LARGE WATERBIRDS, such as geese and swans, are known to frequently "attack" people who feed them, especially small children and people in small boats. Domestic pets are another target for these feisty birds.

MASKED LAPWINGS (*Vanellus miles*) make a noisy, penetrating "kekekekek" call. Lapwings nest in a shallow depression or scrape made on the ground (below). Using spurs on their wings, parent birds aggressively guard their nests and chicks from potential threats and attackers. Their breeding season lasts from late spring to autumn. Unlike magpies, it is very rare for lapwings to strike during an attack.

THE MAGPIE BREEDING SEASON begins in July and the chicks fledge during February. Most magpie attacks occur between August and November when there are chicks in the nest.

MAGPIES SEEM TO GET PARTICULARLY INFURIATED by bicycles. Nearly half the recorded attacks occurred on people who were riding a bike at the time.

BIRDS HAVE GOOD REASON to fear humans. Since the year 1500, more than 140 bird species have become extinct and many more are under threat.

During the breeding season birds can be very territorial. Some will aggressively defend their nests against intruders, although the "attacks" are intended to intimidate and often fall short of an actual strike. If captured, all birds will struggle, bite, peck, grab and scratch.

From late spring to early summer each year, Australians start scanning the skies in anticipation of aerial attacks from Australian Magpies (*Gymnorhina tibicen*) and the related butcherbirds (*Cracticus* spp.). A national survey has found that 90% of Australian males and 72% of females have been attacked by a magpie at some time in their life!

Right: An Australian Magpie at its nest. Magpies are notoriously aggressive during the breeding season.

AERIAL ATTACKS

Magpie and butcherbird attacks can do real damage because the birds often target the face and eyes. Studies have shown that attacks are not random. Most are directed at the same small group of people over and over again. Magpies seem to be able to recognise and remember individual human faces.

It is thought that the birds may have had an early traumatic experience with humans, or come to regard specific people as predators. Only about 12% of all male magpies are responsible for attacks on people — 50% attack only pedestrians; 10% attack postal workers on bikes; 8% attack cyclists; and the remaining 32% will attack any of these.

Almost 66% of magpie victims are male, and 50% of all those attacked were aged between 10–30. Obviously magpies are selective!

Left: Magpies always attack repeatedly from above, either from a high perch or while hovering over an intruder.

Precautions

Never interfere with a bird's nest, eggs or chicks. Do not approach large birds (such as Emus). Keep a wary eye on the sky during breeding seasons and, if necessary, take another route to avoid attacks.

Emus are considered to be the world's second largest living bird after the Ostrich (*Struthio camelus*). Males are responsible for incubating the 20 large green eggs laid by the female.

The Southern Cassowary looks like a short, heavily built, black and blue Emu. These two species of large flightless bird are closely related and belong to the family Casuariidae.

the FACTS!

EMUS CAN RUN AT SPEEDS of up to 50 km/h. At full pace, their stride can reach up to 3 m and they can travel 15–25 km per day.

MANY SPECIES of bird defend their nests and some waterfowl, falcons and large honeyeaters may be even more aggressive than magpies or lapwings. However, these birds are not a "problem" because they locate their nests in accessible areas or simply just defend the nest itself.

CASSOWARIES FIGHT by leaping into the air and kicking forward, sometimes with both feet. The middle toe on a cassowary's foot can reach 12 cm in length and the innermost of its three toes has a long sharp claw about 8 cm long (left). Fights between cassowaries do not usually last long and the birds are rarely injured.

FLIGHTLESS ATTACKS

Like the Southern Cassowary, the Emu (*Dromaius novaehollandiae*) is flightless. It is Australia's tallest native bird, reaching 2 m when standing erect and weighing up to 45 kg. Emus are found across most of the continent. They prefer dry open forest and woodland.

Most people see Emus along roadsides, near fences or other barriers, which gives the impression that they are not afraid of humans. Emus can be bold, curious and unpredictable in their encounters with people. If threatened, Emus will often run away in a zig zag pattern, but their main defence is to kick out with their powerful legs and strong claws. They will also peck.

Emus eat fruits, seeds, growing shoots of plants, insects and other small animals. They are nomadic and will move hundreds of kilometres in search of food and water.

POWERFUL KICKS

Southern Cassowaries (*Casuarius casuarius*) are large, flightless inhabitants of the rainforests and scrubs of north Queensland. They have powerful claws and strong beaks. The biggest Southern Cassowaries are females, which can weigh up to 60 kg and stand nearly 1.8 m tall.

If disturbed, cassowaries will make a low rumbling sound and then intimidate the intruder by standing tall, raising their feathers, hissing and stamping.

If this fails, the birds usually flee. Cornered or injured cassowaries may attack, kicking out with their long, powerful legs and feet, which are armed with tapering, dagger-like claws.

Cassowaries have been described as "rainforest gardeners" because they disperse the seeds of rainforest plants.

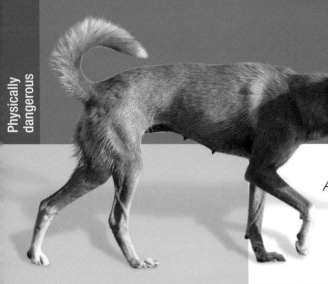

Mammals
— icons & pests

Australia's native mammals are one of the most endearing groups of animals and most pose little or no threat to humans, simply because they are quite small. They also have secretive habits and are difficult to observe in the wild, so there is less chance of adverse interaction with humans.

the FACTS!

A BITE FROM A KANGAROO may cause more damage than a bite from a horse because of its very sharp incisor teeth.

ALTHOUGH KANGAROOS AND WALLABIES have caused many injuries, only one person is known to have been killed by a kangaroo. In 1936, a hunter died of head injuries caused when he approached a kangaroo that had been bailed up by his dogs.

IN GOOD SEASONS when food is plentiful, the native Long-haired Rat (*Rattus villosissimus*, below) sometimes occurs in plague numbers in Central Australia. As the seasons turn and food again becomes scarce, the starving rats have reportedly attacked the hooves of sleeping cattle and lamed them.

Wild kangaroos are shy and will rarely allow humans to approach closely. These Red Kangaroos (*Macropus rufus*) have been alerted to the photographer's presence but are not yet ready to flee.

THEIR ATTRACTIVE APPEARANCE and the seemingly placid nature of our native mammals belies the fact that even the tiniest planigale will fight viciously in self-defence. A person, who is wary about handling a rat "because it might bite", will often show less caution when it comes to "cute and cuddly" mammals.

Most human injuries come from bites and scratches from just a few larger mammal species, including Dingoes, kangaroos, wombats and several feral species. Occasionally, secondary infections from bacteria in the wound are a problem and disease, particularly from bats, is also a risk. Mammals have caused human deaths, but this is rare.

BITING, SCRATCHING & KICKING

Wombats (*Vombatus* and *Lasiorhinus* spp.) are definitely "cute and cuddly". Wild animals often show little fear of humans and will even allow themselves to be touched, but wombats can be very bad-tempered. They will attack intruders, such as dogs, that enter their burrows by crushing them against the burrow walls. Hand-raised wombats are notorious biters of legs, feet and hands.

Kangaroos and wallabies (macropods) should always be treated with caution. They can deliver vicious bites with their sharp incisor teeth and slashing kicks with the enlarged toe and toe nail of the hind foot. Male combat is a natural behaviour of these animals, but sometimes this aggression can be directed at nearby humans.

Precautions

Many mammals will bite if handled or provoked. Large mammals can inflict powerful bites, kicks and scratches. Beware of close contact. The standard rule applies — look, but do not touch.

CENTRE: QM-BC

DINGOES & DOGS

From the earliest days of European settlement, Australia's wild dog, the Dingo (*Canis lupus dingo*) has been considered a savage animal, not safe for livestock or humans. Any attack by a Dingo usually generates public alarm and provokes heated debate about its place in the environment and how to best manage the animal.

Dingoes have been responsible for serious and sometimes fatal attacks on humans of all ages, but attacks by Domestic Dogs (*Canis lupus familiaris*) are far more frequent. At least 80% of all reported animal bite injuries are from domestic dogs, with about 30,000 people requiring treatment at Australian hospitals each year.

The Dingo is a very controversial animal. Some wildlife experts even argue that it should not be regarded as a native animal.

Wild Dingoes are normally wary, suspicious creatures and unprovoked attacks are rare. This situation changes when Dingoes become accustomed to humans, losing their natural fear. If Dingoes are hand-fed, or are allowed to scavenge too close to human habitation, camping grounds or picnic areas, this greatly increases the risk to people.

the FACTS!

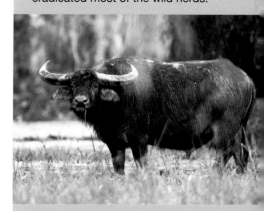

FERAL MAMMALS

Feral Pigs (*Sus scrofa*) and Swamp Buffalo (*Bubalus bubalis*) are large, unpredictable feral animals and both are serious environmental pests. Most attacks by pigs and buffalo occur when they are being hunted, but unprovoked attacks have been recorded.

Feral Pigs have been described as "lean and mean" with some justification. Pigs have long lower incisors (tusks) that constantly grow. An attacking pig will bite and use its tusks as slashing weapons.

Water Buffalo are armed with a set of thick, curved horns. They use their horns and weight to batter, trample and gore. Unprovoked buffalo attacks, mainly by bulls, are likely to occur if people approach too closely, or if the animal has already been injured.

Left: Feral Pigs damage natural habitats and farmland by selective feeding, trampling and digging for plants and animals. They cause extensive damage in and around watercourses, moist gullies, swamps and lagoons.

FERAL PIGS are opportunistic omnivores. In addition to small invertebrates, green vegetation, animals, fruits, roots, bulbs and grain, they will also eat fungi, earthworms, snails, frogs, eggs of ground-nesting birds, turtle eggs, lambs and carrion. Like domestic pigs, feral pigs need a diet high in protein (more than 15%) in order to breed and raise their young.

Sponges
— not so soft

the FACTS!

SPONGES BELONG to the phylum Porifera (from the Latin words *porus* — meaning "pore" — and *ferre* — meaning "to bear"). The word describes the surface of a sponge.

A SPONGE IS BASICALLY a loose grouping of different cells. Each group of cells undertakes specific tasks for the animal, but some are able to change their function as needed. These cells can build skeletons, form the outer layer of the animal or become feeding cells.

MOST SPONGES are risky to handle because of their sharp spicules, which are part of the sponge skeleton, and the organisms that group on their surfaces (such as stinging anemones).

THE SPONGE *Neofibularia irata*, is known as the Touch-me-not because of the pain it causes people who touch it.

SPONGES HAVE COMPLEX water canal systems running throughout their bodies. They can actively pump up to ten times their body volume each hour, making them the most efficient vacuum cleaners in the sea.

Sea creatures produce some of the deadliest venoms known. None of these animals hunt humans, so people are only at risk when they handle or unexpectedly come into contact with them.

MANY MARINE ANIMALS, such as sponges, corals and anemones, are sedentary creatures. This means they spend part, or all of their lives, fixed to one spot. Animals that are unable to move often use chemical defences to keep threats at bay.

CLEVER SPONGES

Sponges are the most primitive multicellular animals (metazoa). They live in water and most are ocean-dwellers. Sponges are familiar to most people as dried, colourless bath sponges, but in water their shapes and colours are as varied as the animals around them.

Sponges are potentially valuable sources of chemical compounds for medical purposes. As filter-feeders, they extract nutrients from water as it flows through their bodies. In this way, they are able to modify toxins released into the water by other animals. Sponges also produce their own chemicals for protection. These same toxins make touching the surface of some sponges hazardous for humans.

Touch-me-not Sponge (*Neofibularia irata*)

Another potential danger lies in the small needle-like structures (spicules) that form part of a sponge's mineral "skeleton". Spicules can be sharp and also carry toxins. Sometimes contact with a sponge does not cause any immediate reaction. Stinging and prickly or itchy sensations are often felt some time later and, in extreme cases, rashes and blistering may occur and continue for months.

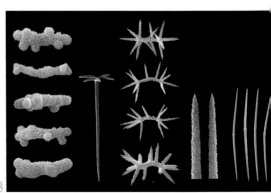

Above: Pink tubular sponge (*Dactylia* sp.)
Right: Examples of sponge spicules.

Cnidarians
— beautiful stingers

Cnidarians are a beautiful and diverse group of aquatic animals. They often have bright colours and fantastic shapes. All have tentacles armed with stinging cells (nematocysts) to capture their prey.

CORALS, ANEMONES, BOX JELLIES, HYDROIDS AND TRUE SEA JELLIES are all cnidarians. Although they may seem quite different, cnidarians have two basic body shapes. Some, like sea jellies, are free-swimming medusae with tentacles attached to a central "bell". Others, like corals and anemones, are tubular polyps that attach to rocks, coral or the sea floor. They have a central mouth surrounded by tentacles on the top of their bodies.

Soft corals are an important part of coral reefs. In some areas, they form dense growths that resemble fields of wildflowers.

the FACTS!

THE WORD CNIDARIAN comes from the Greek *cnidos*, which means "stinging needle".

THE STINGS OF ANEMONES are fatal to many small marine animals, but some fish and shrimps manage to live among the stinging tentacles and rarely stray far from them. This Pink Anemonefish (*Amphiprion perideraion*, below) is protected from the stings of this Magnificent Sea Anemone (*Heteractis magnifica*) by a thick layer of mucus on its skin, but each individual must slowly accustom itself to a particular anemone.

NEMATOCYSTS are specialised cells that each contain a spring-loaded, pressure-sensitive tube that delivers the venom. The thread-like tube is coiled and barbed and when triggered it "fires" venom into an attacker or prey animal.

Below: Discharged (left) and undischarged (right) nematocyst.

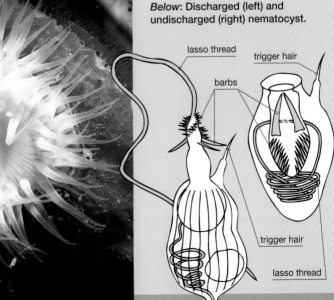

lasso thread

trigger hair

barbs

trigger hair

lasso thread

PREDATORY FLOWERS

Anemones are often referred to as the "flowers" of the sea because of their beautiful colours and soft, flower-like forms. The "petals" that crown the top of anemones are actually the tentacles that carry stinging cells.

Sea anemones are predators. Any fish or small marine animal that ventures too close to their tentacles risks being stung and devoured. Most are harmless to humans. However, some can cause skin irritations and occasionally severe pain, blisters and breathing difficulties. "Stinging" sea anemones occur in tropical and temperate waters around Australia.

Precautions

Look but never touch. Apply first aid for all stings and cuts. Seek medical attention immediately.

Cnidarians
— hydrozoans

Hydrozoans are sometimes described as "pests in paradise". Many species occur as part of the vibrant, colourful ecosystems on coral reefs and in warm tropical waters, but just brushing against a hydrozoan can cause instant pain.

the FACTS!

FIRE CORALS are aptly named because of the burning sensation they cause when touched.

THE VELELLA (*Velella velella*, below) is a close relative of the Portuguese Man-of-War. It consists of a flat disc with an erect "sail" running across it. The animal floats on the currents and, like the Portuguese Man-of-War, is often beach-washed after strong winds in northern Australia. It is also known as a By-the-wind Sailor.

FIRE CORALS OF THE GENUS *Millepora* are typically green in colour.

THE CYPRESS SEA FERN (*Aglaophenia cupressina*) is the largest stinging sea fern found in tropical waters. It grows to 60 cm.

The White Stinging Sea Fern (*Macrorhynchia philippina*) inhabits tropical and subtropical coral reefs. Even the slightest brush against bare skin will produce painful stings.

LIKE OTHER CNIDARIANS, hydrozoans have an astonishing array of colours and shapes. Some build colonies resembling plants or corals. Other colonies look like sea jellies and are free-swimming. A few live solitary lives as individual polyps.

Sea fern colonies typically grow in a branching pattern with delicate fronds and feathery filaments. Each "frond" contains thousands of polyps. "Hydrocorals" (fire and lace corals) resemble hard corals in appearance and some even excrete a bony skeleton. They are an integral part of reef environments.

Within a hydrozoan colony, different groups of polyps perform different tasks, such as capturing prey, digesting food, defending the colony and reproducing. Sedentary hydrozoans often live under coral or rock overhangs, near the mouth of underwater caves, or near jetty pylons, where the swirling water currents ensure a plentiful supply of food.

PESKY BLUEBOTTLES

The brilliant colouring of the Portuguese Man-of-War (*Physalia physalis*) gives these animals their other common name of "Bluebottle". Although they look like sea jellies, these animals are hydrozoan colonies. The "float", which supports the colony, is formed by a single polyp, and other polyps make up the rest of the "body". Sea jellies are single animals.

Bluebottles are the scourge of Australian beaches, being responsible for more stings than any other cnidarian. Their tentacles trail below the "float" and the sharp, painful sting is followed by redness, aches, blisters and welts.

Bluebottles have sufficient venom-filled nematocysts to paralyse and kill any small creatures they come into contact with.

Cnidarians
— corals

Precautions

Look but never touch. Exercise caution and wear shoes when walking on coral. Apply first aid and seek medical attention immediately.

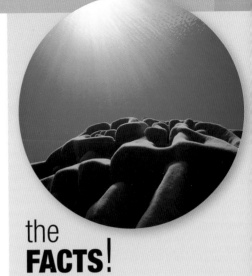

Hard corals are probably the most familiar cnidarians because of the amazing stony reefs they build. Australia's Great Barrier Reef, the largest structure built by living organisms on Earth, is the work of billions of tiny coral polyps over thousands of years.

REEF-FORMING POLYPS live in extensive colonies. Each polyp extracts calcium carbonate from the seawater to build a limestone "skeleton" around itself for protection. Layers of these "skeletons" ultimately form coral reefs.

Hard corals have rough, abrasive surfaces and razor-sharp edges. Coral polyps are too tiny to seriously sting humans. The real hazard is that cuts or scrapes can become infected from limestone fragments, micro-organisms and organic material on the surface of the coral. Signs of secondary infection include redness, swelling and warmth. Two of the bacteria responsible for infections are *Staphylococcus aureus* and *Vibrio vulnificus*.

the FACTS!

MANY CNIDARIANS, particularly corals, have symbiotic algae, known as zooxanthellae, living inside their bodies. The algae help provide nutrients or energy for the cnidarians, which in turn provide protection for the algae. The zooxanthellae give corals their beautiful colours.

Hard corals come in many shapes and forms. All have rough abrasive surfaces and sharp edges. Delicate and branching corals may be very brittle.

THE GREAT BARRIER REEF

The Great Barrier Reef, which stretches more than 2300 km along the coast of Queensland in north-eastern Australia, is not a single continuous reef. It consists of more than 2900 individual reefs and coral cays and about 600 islands.

The reef supports 300 hard coral species, thousands of other cnidarian species, 1500 fish species, 4000 mollusc species and more than 200 bird species. The Great Barrier Reef is the world's largest coral reef ecosystem and was declared a World Heritage Area in 1981.

Left: Although the surface of a coral reef at low tide appears to be rock-like and solid, parts of it are likely to be brittle and crumbly underfoot.

MOST HARD CORALS build reefs in warm shallow waters, but some solitary species occur in cold waters at depths of around 2000 m.

ALTHOUGH CORAL COLONIES are immobile, they have the ability to strike at neighbouring colonies. They use long sweeper "tentacles" that can reach several centimetres to attack competitors.

Cnidarians
— sea jellies

Sea jellies ("jellyfish") are free-swimming or floating cnidarians. They are mainly encountered in marine waters, but a few species live in freshwater. Fortunately, most jellies are harmless, but some can deliver painful and even fatal stings.

the FACTS!

SEA JELLIES ARE EATEN by a number of large marine animals, including Leatherback Turtles (*Dermochelys coriacea*) and Ocean Sunfish (*Mola mola*).

TO MARINE ANIMALS, PLASTIC BAGS looks like sea jellies. Plastic bags will remain in the gut of sea creatures and can be fatal. Marine animals also confuse rubber, balloons and confectionery wrappers with food. Avoid littering beaches and dumping rubbish from boats.

IRUKANDJI SYNDROME is a severe medical condition caused by box jelly stings. The sting may not be immediately painful. After a while the victim experiences severe pain in their head, back, chest, abdomen and muscles. Other symptoms follow, including nausea and restlessness. In susceptible individuals, complications can prove fatal.

SCIENTISTS originally believed that a small carybdeid box jelly, *Carukia barnesi*, was responsible for the condition. Its bell is only 1–2 cm across, but its four tentacles can trail up to 1 m. The animals are found mostly in deep reef waters, but wind sometimes sweeps them inshore. It is now thought that several different species of sea jelly cause Irukandji Syndrome.

SEA JELLIES RANGE from delicate gossamer bells that trail long, wispy tentacles to large blubbery masses with thick clusters of stubby, finger-like tentacles. Some have transparent bodies, while others are highly coloured and ornate, with a "frill" between the upper bell and the lower tentacles. There are three groups — "true" sea jellies, "box" jellies (or sea wasps) and hydromedusae.

Some animals are not only immune to stinging sea jellies, they are able to eat them and absorb the poisonous compounds to use for their own defence. For example, some nudibranchs (sea slugs) that prey on sea jellies can even recycle the stinging nematocysts. The bright blue or violet "sea lizards" (*Glaucus* spp.), do this so effectively that they sting by touch.

"TRUE" SEA JELLIES

The "true" sea jellies are the animals that are most familiar to beach-goers. They include the Lion's Mane (or Hair) Sea Jelly (*Cyanea capillata*), sea nettles (*Chrysaora* spp.), upside-down sea jellies (*Cassiopeia* spp.), "blubbers" (*Catostylus mosaicus*) and the Moon Jelly (*Aurelia aurita*).

The jellies drift at the mercy of the currents, often accumulating in sheltered bays and estuaries. They "swim" using a pumping motion, which does little more than move them up or down in the water. In Australia "true" sea jellies can deliver unpleasant or severe stings (causing cramps, coughing, blistering and long-lasting pain); fortunately, however, there have not been any recorded fatalities.

RON & VALERIE TAYLOR

Timoides agassizii is an example of a hydromedusa. These jellies are smaller and more delicate than "true" sea jellies or box jellies. They are the sexual reproductive stage of hydrozoans.

RON & VALERIE TAYLOR

Sea jellies can be delicate and ethereal creatures. Many are transparent and barely visible as they drift in the water.

Precautions

Never swim alone, or outside protected areas. Douse the victim with vinegar to deactivate the nematocysts. Apply first aid and seek medical attention immediately.

NASTY JELLIES

Sea wasps or "box" jellies can be distinguished from sea jellies by their square, or cube-shaped, bell. Only 30 species are known, but they include some of the most dangerous of all marine animals.

True sea jellies are blind "drifters" that must wait for hapless prey to blunder into their tentacles. In contrast, box jellies have primitive "eyes" on each side of the bell so they can hunt and avoid objects in the water. They are also capable of swimming at a speed of about 3 knots (approximately 5.5 km/h).

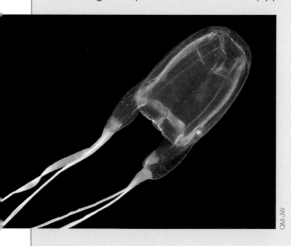

QM-JW

The two main families of box jelly are the Chirodropidae and Carybdeidae. Chirodropidae have multiple tentacles hanging from each corner of their bell. Carybdeidae have a single tentacle hanging from each corner.

The box jellies of the genus *Tamoya* are mainly found in tropical waters. *Tamoya virulenta* is one species that can be encountered in southern Queensland waters. Like all carybdeids, it has four tentacles that are capable of delivering a very painful sting.

DEADLY JELLY

The Box Jelly (*Chironex fleckeri*) is probably the world's deadliest marine animal. It is common in northern Australian waters in the warmer months of the year. The jelly measures up to 20 cm along each side of its bell and has as many as fifteen tentacles, which trail 3 m behind or below the bell.

Box Jellies seem to move inshore in calm waters on the rising tide and gather near the mouths of rivers, estuaries and creeks following rain. Beaches are often closed during "stinger season" and protective nets have been installed at many popular tourist destinations in northern Australia. Some people wear specially designed, cover-all swimming costumes for further protection.

Right: More than 60 people are known to have died after being stung by a Box Jelly, sometimes within minutes of the attack.

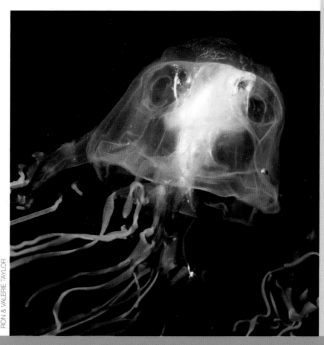

RON & VALERIE TAYLOR

the FACTS!

EACH TENTACLE of a Box Jelly is armed with an estimated 5000 nematocysts.

CARYBDEA RASTONI is the only box jelly regularly recorded from the cooler waters of southern Australia. Its sting is only noticeable on sensitive areas like the lips.

OVERFISHING of sea jelly predators, damage to marine environments and global warming appear to be causing a rise in sea jelly populations. Dramatic increases ("blooms") of sea jellies have been reported worldwide.

RON & VALERIE TAYLOR

SEA JELLIES range in size from 12 mm to the Giant Lion's Mane Sea Jelly (*Cyanea arctica*) of Northern Hemisphere waters. This jelly has tentacles more than 40 m long and measures more than 2 m across the bell!

THE BOX JELLY swims with a jet-like pumping motion. The season for the Box Jelly starts with the onset of the wet season across the top of northern Australia and lasts until autumn.

THE UPSIDE-DOWN sea jellies rest upside-down on their bell, tentacles pointing up on seagrass meadows or sandy and muddy bottoms near mangroves.

Precautions

Look but don't touch. Apply first aid; seek medical attention immediately.

Sea urchins
— living pincushions

RON & VALERIE TAYLOR

Sea stars, sea urchins, feather stars, brittle stars and sea cucumbers belong to a group of slow-moving marine animals that have unusual body shapes. The scientific name for this phylum — Echinodermata — comes from the Greek word for "spiny skin".

the FACTS!

ABOUT 800 SPECIES of echinoderm occur on Australia's Great Barrier Reef.

ECHINODERMS have an unusual body plan and lack a head or tail. They have a network of water-filled tubes (a "vascular system") that stick out through their "skin" forming "tube feet". The animal is able to control the water pressure within the network and the tube feet act like tiny, hydraulically operated legs to power its movement.

SAND DOLLARS have a limited degree of movement and spend most of their time half-buried in the sediments of the sea floor. Heart urchins burrow through the sediments and are completely buried for most of their lives.

SEA URCHINS ARE SOLITARY animals that may live in loose groups. They are active at night and feed on algae, seaweed, seagrass, flesh and decaying organic matter. During the day, sea urchins will wedge themselves into rock or coral crevices and under ledges.

SEA URCHINS, SAND DOLLARS AND HEART URCHINS have a rounded skeleton covered in rough skin and a dense coat of spines. Urchin spines are usually brittle, sharp and barbed. They act as an impenetrable barrier against most threats and will even penetrate a diver's wetsuit.

The spines can be long and needle-like, or thick as a pencil. Very fine spines give some urchins a "hairy" or "bristly" look. The spines are easily broken and embedded in skin, but can be difficult to remove. Touching or stepping on the spines will cause a painful puncture wound that often becomes infected. Sea urchins can be black, purple, brown or white.

RON & VALERIE TAYLOR

The Fire Urchin (*Asthenosoma varium*) is aptly named because of its intensely painful sting.

TOXIC SPINES

Sea urchins don't rely solely on their sharp spines for defence. Several species, including the Banded Sea Urchin (*Echinothrix calamaris*), have "stinging" spines covered in harmful toxins. In some, the spines are tipped with balloon-like venom sacs that deliver a sting, but do not puncture the skin.

Other sea urchins have a venomous "bite", courtesy of tiny pincer-like structures (pedicellariae) located on their outer surface among the spines. Venomous urchins, such as the Flower Sea Urchin (*Toxopneustes pileolus*), have pedicellariae that are linked to poison sacs.

RON & VALERIE TAYLOR

Flower Sea Urchins are the most venomous of their kind. Their pedicellariae continue to inject venom even when detached from the urchin.

Sea stars
& sea cucumbers

Precautions
Look but don't touch.
Apply first aid; seek
medical attention
immediately.

Perhaps the most familiar of all echinoderms are the sea stars ("starfish"), named for their star-shaped bodies. Sea star spines can penetrate wet suits and gloves and some species also have toxic mucus that affects exposed skin.

A MAJOR THREAT
TO MANY

The infamous Crown-of-Thorns Sea Star (*Acanthaster planci*) is probably the best known species — for all the wrong reasons. This creature is responsible for devastating attacks on coral reefs and is also the sea star that causes the most injuries to people.

The Crown-of-Thorns Sea Star is unusually large and grows to more than 40 cm in diameter. It has up to 21 arms covered in long venomous spines. The spines are covered in glandular cells that produce a variety of toxins that cause extreme pain. Wounds can take several months to heal.

This sea star is a major threat to the Great Barrier Reef, where it feeds on coral polyps and leaves a trail of bleached white coral in its wake.

RON & VALERIE TAYLOR

the FACTS!

LIKE ALL ECHINODERMS, sea stars move using their tube feet.

THERE ARE THREE CLASSES of sea star — feather stars (class: Crinoidea), sea stars (class: Asteroidea) and brittle stars (class: Ophiuroidea). Feather stars are a mass of brightly coloured feather-like arms that radiate from a tiny cup-like body. Sea stars have five (sometimes more) radiating limbs and are covered in plates that makes them appear quite rigid. Brittle stars have a central, disc-like body and usually five, snake-like, branched or feathery limbs.

SEA STARS HAVE EXCELLENT POWERS of regeneration and are able to regrow arms bitten off by predators. Some brittle stars will even shed all or part of an arm when disturbed or attacked.

SEA CUCUMBERS belong to the class Holothuroidea. There are 1150 species of sea cucumber worldwide.

TOXIC CUCUMBERS

Sea cucumbers are large, sausage-shaped echinoderms. They have tough skins, but rely on a very different means of defence. Sea cucumbers can eject their entire digestive system, or a mass of fine sticky threads (Cuvierian tubules) from their rear end to distract or deter predators.

Most sea cucumbers are generally regarded as non-venomous and harmless, but some species secrete poisonous mucus or have toxic Cuvierian tubules. Contact with either will result in severe skin irritation, dermatitis and eye injury.

Sea cucumbers are often referred to as "vacuum cleaners of the sea" for their habit of mopping up debris that collect on the sea floor.

QM-JW

Marine worms
— dazzling variety

Although they are often overlooked, worms are a diverse group of soft-bodied animals that inhabit almost every environment on Earth. On land, worms pose little health risk to humans and the main threat comes from species that are parasites.

IN AQUATIC ENVIRONMENTS, however, worms are far more diverse and have an amazing variety of body shapes. They are an important part of the food chain for young fish and other animals. Like their land-based relatives, most are harmless, but a few species are large enough to bite and some have needle-sharp spines or bristles.

OM-JW

the FACTS!

CLAM WORMS feed at night and shelter during the day in transparent, mucus-lined sand burrows. They are swift, voracious predators that use a keen sense of smell to find prey. They will attack other worms, small crustaceans, molluscs (including clams) and other small animals. Clam worms have strong jaws and can bite.

MARINE WORMS BELONG to ten different phyla. They can be found in all marine habitats and at all depths. Some are long and thin, some are segmented (phylum: Annelida), while others are ribbon-like (phylum: Nemertea) or flat (phylum: Platyhelminthes). Their colours vary from dull to bright.

MARINE FLATWORMS (order: Polycladida, below) are mostly found on sea floor habitats (although a few float near the surface. Many polyclad species are brightly coloured and resemble the flattened, shell-less, nudibranch molluscs, which are not worms at all.

Marine worms come in many forms, shapes and colours. Most, like the Christmas Tree Worm (*Spirobranchus giganteus*), are harmless.

MICE OF THE SEA

Sea mice are slow-moving bottom-dwellers. They grow to about 10–20 cm long and their rounded shape and "furry" upper surface gives them a passing resemblance to a mouse. The "fur" is actually numerous fine, silky bristles (chaetae).The bristles on a sea mouse can be easily dislodged, resulting in painful irritation and infection for any animal that attempts to prey on it. Most sea mouse species occur in shallow water below the tidal zone and a few are found in deep water. Sea mice eat other worms and small, soft-bodied animals.

Precautions
Look but don't touch. Apply first aid;
seek medical attention immediately.

BRISTLEWORMS

Bristleworms are free-swimming predators that usually inhabit shallow water. They have brightly coloured elongated bodies and tufts of whitish bristles (chaetae) along each side.

A large bristleworm will bite if handled, but it is the tufts of bristles along its sides that pose a greater threat. Each tuft is comprised of many tiny, sharp spines that look a bit like the threads of fibreglass. The hollow, brittle spines are toxic and snap off on contact. Once embedded, they are difficult to remove, causing intense pain.

Bloodworms (*Marphysa* spp.) "bleed" if they break, hence their common name. Bloodworms are also a type of bristleworm and are common in intertidal zones along the east coast of Australia.

the FACTS!

BRISTLEWORMS ARE COMMON around rocks and coral reefs and often burrow into the sediment or sandy bottom. Some species gather together under boulders and coral, while others construct burrows for shelter.

IT IS THOUGHT that each tuft of spines on a bristleworm has its own venom gland. Bristleworms not only have their own chemical defences, some of the coral-feeding species incorporate the coral's stinging defences into their own arsenal.

THE GIANT BEACH or "bungum" worms (*Australonuphis* spp.) are predators and scavengers that lurk around the low water mark of sandy and surf beaches from Queensland to South Australia. The two species, *Australonuphis teres* and *Australonuphis parateres*, are both highly valued as bait.

THE CURRENT METHOD of collecting beachworms involves extracting them by hand, one worm at a time. Although some beaches have been heavily "fished" for a long time, the worms remain plentiful. It is thought that this is due to the harvesting technique, which causes virtually no habitat disturbance. However, mass collection of beachworms using mechanical diggers and similar devices is unlikely to be as sustainable.

FIRE WORMS

The Fire Worm (*Eurythoe complanata*) is aptly named because it is probably responsible for more stings than any other Australian worm. A type of bristleworm, it is common in tropical and subtropical waters and favours sandy bottoms and rocky and coral reefs. Fire Worms are often found under coral slabs and boulders and many stings occur when people lift lumps of coral or rock and touch the sand underneath. The venomous spines of this worm are so fine and sharp that they can penetrate thin plastic or rubber gloves. Electric bristleworms (*Eurythoe* spp.) also inhabit sandy areas and are armed with similar venomous spines.

The Fire Worm is common under rocks and rubble in muddy sand. It occurs across northern Australia.

BEACH WORMS

Beachworms are gigantic animals more than 1 m long with pale golden bristles down the sides. They are popular as bait and can be caught by dragging a dead fish along the edge of the surf and then grabbing the head of the worm as it surfaces to feed. For the unwary, this sometimes means a sharp nip because the worms have powerful jaws.

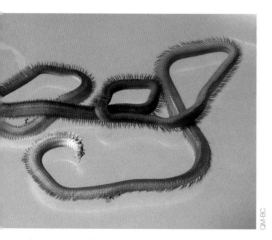

Beachworms (*Australonuphis* spp.) live mostly in the intertidal zone of ocean beaches.

Precautions

Never pick up cone shells. Apply first aid; seek medical attention immediately.

Cone shells
— deadly hunters

The world's oceans are home to some of the most spectacularly coloured animals on Earth, but a beautiful exterior often masks unsuspected danger. The bright colours that make an animal stand out from its surroundings usually mean it has little to fear from predators. Cone shells are no exception.

the FACTS!

THE STRIATED CONE (*Conus striatus*, above) lives in sand pockets under corals and rocks.

THE THEORY that picking up cone shells by their blunt end is a safe practice, isn't true. Cones can extend their proboscis. The shells should not be placed in a wetsuit, or in a pocket, as the animal's harpoon can pierce neoprene and clothing.

THE VENOM APPARATUS of a cone shell is coiled and twisted inside the shell and can be more than five times the animal's length. The cone shell "stores" a couple of teeth inside and then "charges" them with venom before use.

MOLLUSC AND FISH-EATING CONES are dangerous to humans. The most dangerous is the Geography Cone (*Conus geographus*), which is known to have caused at least twelve fatal stings. The radular dart of this cone can penetrate gloves and wetsuits.

THE ANEMONE CONE (*Conus anemone*) is one of the few cone shell species commonly found along the southern coastline of Australia.

BASED ON DIET, there are three different cone shell groups — worm-eaters, fish-eaters and gastropod-eaters (which also feed on other cone shells as well). Cone shell teeth vary according to the animal's prey. Cones that feed on worms have short serrated teeth, while cones that feed on fish have smooth, elongated teeth and a sharp barb at the end.

THE LARGE SIZE, beauty and intricate patterns of cones have made them popular with collectors for hundreds of years. They are also among the deadliest marine creatures, releasing potent venoms that can kill a human being. Despite the temptation, cone shells should never be picked up.

Cones are marine "snails". More than 500 species occur worldwide, with about 80 in Australia. Most are tropical animals although a few occur in cooler, temperate waters. They inhabit coral and rocky reefs and gravel, mud or sand flats and are also found among underwater vegetation and rubble. Cones are active at night, hiding under coral slabs, or burying in sand during the day.

All species of cones should be treated as potentially dangerous.

Left: Cones range in size from 25–200 mm. Many cones, particularly the widespread tropical species, vary in shape and colour.

SPEAR-LIKE TEETH

Cone shells are carnivorous, preying on other marine animals (including, worms, molluscs and small fish).

Cone shells have an extendable proboscis, which they eject from the narrow end of the shell. The proboscis is armed with spear-like, hollow teeth that are used like darts to inject venom into the cone shell's victims.

Only one tooth, located at the tip of the proboscis, is used each time. After the prey is speared, the proboscis is drawn back into the mouth and the prey is then digested.

Right: Diagram of venom-delivery system of a cone shell.

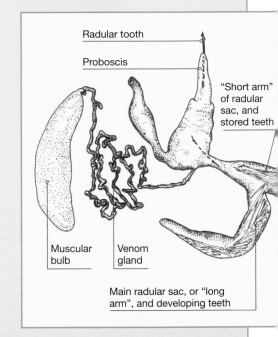

Radular tooth

Proboscis

"Short arm" of radular sac, and stored teeth

Muscular bulb

Venom gland

Main radular sac, or "long arm", and developing teeth

Blue-ringed octopus
— small but lethal

Precautions
Look but never touch.
Apply first aid; seek medical
attention immediately.

Venomous

Octopuses, squids and cuttlefish belong to the same phylum as cone shells — the molluscs — but they have little use for shells. Instead of a protective hard shell, octopuses and their relatives have a number of other effective defence mechanisms.

Seven species of blue-ringed octopus (*Hapalochlaena* spp.) inhabit Australian waters. They are very common in shallow waters around the coast. *Hapalochlaena maculosa* grows up to 20 cm across its stretched tentacles and is commonly found on coral reefs.

RON & VALERIE TAYLOR

the FACTS!

BLUE-RINGED OCTOPUSES are carnivorous. Two large salivary glands provide powerful venom via the salivary duct to the mouth, which has two beak-like jaws. There are no fangs and the venom enters the wound as saliva, rather than being injected. Blue-ringed octopuses are normally not aggressive and attack only when provoked.

BLUE-RINGED OCTOPUS VENOM is produced by bacteria that live in the salivary glands. All species, including the Blue-lined Octopus (below), inject this venom through bites from a small parrot-like beak.

THESE DEFENCES include an ability to change their colour, texture, and apparent size; expel an inky "smoke-screen"; and employ jet propulsion for a quick "getaway". Although octopuses in general possess beaks and salivary glands that secrete toxins fatal to many crustaceans, they usually do not affect humans. The exceptions are the beautiful blue-ringed octopuses. All species are dangerous and they have caused at least two fatalities and several near fatalities.

Blue-ringed octopuses are small animals, measuring no more than 15 cm across their outspread tentacles. They are mottled yellowish-brown with dark brown bands and irregular faint blue circles scattered over the tentacles and blue rings or lines on the body. When an individual is disturbed, these colours darken and the rings become a vivid peacock blue.

Left: The Blue-lined Octopus (*Hapalochlaena fasciata*) is so-named because it shows iridescent blue lines on the body and blue rings on the tentacles when alarmed. This octopus occurs in the subtropical waters of eastern Australia and is often encountered by people in tidal rock pools.

IT IS SAID THAT ONE blue-ringed octopus may contain enough venom to paralyse 10 adult humans. The actual bite is often relatively painless and may go unnoticed. If sufficient venom has been introduced (sometimes little venom may enter the wound if the attack occurs underwater), the victim will notice numbness or tingling around the face and neck within a few minutes.

Spiders
— silk & fangs

People either love spiders or hate them — there's no middle ground. Australia has thousands of different spider species. Most are venomous and a few are dangerous. One species, the Sydney Funnel-web, is considered to be one of the most dangerous spiders in the world.

SPIDER VENOM contains a mixture of toxins that affect different parts of a spider's prey. Spider venom, unlike snake venom, only immobilises prey and plays no part in digestion. Most spiders are secretive animals that rarely come into contact with people, but in general, spiders should be treated with caution and should not be handled.

Fear of spiders is called arachnophobia. It is one of the most common fears among humans.

the FACTS!

THE JUMPING SPIDERS (above) use their strong legs to jump onto passing prey animals. They have excellent eyesight and can turn their heads to look at objects.

SPIDERS COME IN MANY SHAPES and sizes. The smallest are pinhead-sized inhabitants that live in moist leaf litter and moss, while the largest, the Goliath Tarantula (*Theraphosa blondi*), which hails from South America, has a leg span of 30 cm.

GOLDEN ORB-WEAVING SPIDERS (*Nephila* spp.) have been known to successfully capture very small birds that become entangled in the sticky, golden strands of their large webs (below). However, this is not common and most birds can escape after a brief struggle.

PRIMITIVE & TRUE

There are two main types of spider. The mygalomorphs (trapdoors, funnel-webs and tarantulas) are "primitive" animals with fangs that move vertically. They do not produce sticky silk for web-building, but live in silk-lined burrows, silken tubes or behind veils of silk. The araneomorphs are "true" or "modern" spiders. They produce sticky and non-sticky silk and usually construct a web to catch prey.

The venom glands of a mygalomorph, like this trapdoor spider, are located in its fangs.

LEFT & RIGHT: QM-JW

Precautions
Never touch spiders. Apply first aid and seek medical attention immediately.

MOUSE SPIDERS

Mouse spiders (*Missulena* spp.) are widespread across mainland Australia and are common close to homes and gardens. Mouse spiders grow to 3 cm long and are very stocky with short, thick legs. They are often confused with funnel-web spiders. Their venom is as potentially dangerous as that of a funnel-web.

Left: Mouse spiders build short burrows in the ground. The burrows are protected by a floppy door. Juvenile mouse spiders are thought to disperse aerially by silk threads in the wind. This is rare among trapdoor spider species.

QM

the FACTS!

SOME TRAPDOOR SPIDERS have brushes or tufts of hair ("claw tufts") on the ends of the legs that enable them to climb smooth vertical surfaces. Most, like the large male silver-haired brush-footed trapdoor spider (*Idiommata* sp., below), can only climb vertical surfaces slowly, but small ones scoot up glass easily.

QM-GJC

HIGHLY TOXIC VENOM

Funnel-web spiders have a fast-acting, highly toxic venom. At least fifteen species of funnel-web spider (*Atrax* and *Hadronyche* spp.) occur along the east coast of Australia.

Funnel-web spiders have a shiny black thorax and a black or dark plum abdomen. The body of a female funnel-web spider can cover a 50 cent coin; the legs of the largest funnel-webs easily span the width of an adult hand. The Sydney Funnel-web Spider (*Atrax robustus*), which occurs from Newcastle to Nowra and west to Lithgow, is responsible for most bites. Both males and females of all funnel-web species are aggressive. Bites from either sex are potentially dangerous and can cause fatalities. Funnel-web bites are most prevalent during summer and autumn when males leave their burrows in search of females.

Above right: Funnel-web spiders were responsible for fourteen deaths from 1927–1980. The venom of males is more toxic than that of females.

Right: Funnel-web spiders are mostly ground-dwelling and their burrows are lined with tough silk. However, they can also climb trees and the walls of timber houses.

QM

QM-BIC

QM

YOUNG SPIDERS resemble adults. Only their size and colouration differ. Male spiders are usually smaller than female spiders.

IT IS HARD TO DEFINE which spider in the world is the most dangerous to humans. Several spiders could qualify, depending on what is actually meant by "dangerous". For example, those that have powerful venom may not be encountered by humans very often, while others with less powerful venom are responsible for the majority of bites.

THE MOST DANGEROUS spiders in the world are generally thought to be the funnel-web spiders (*Atrax* and *Hadronyche* spp.), the various widow spiders (*Latrodectus* spp.), banana spiders (*Phoneutria* spp.) and recluse spiders (*Loxosceles* spp.).

Spiders
& other arachnids

Thousands of people are bitten by spiders every year in Australia, but only a relatively few bites cause problems. There have been very few deaths from funnel-webs, or the notorious Redback Spider, since the development of antivenoms. Other arachnids that pose a threat to humans include scorpions, ticks, millipedes and centipedes.

the FACTS!

DADDY-LONGLEGS SPIDERS (*Pholcus* spp., below) and White-tailed Spiders are known to catch and kill Redback Spiders.

THE BROWN WIDOW is the most active breeder among widow species, producing up to 5000 young per female per season. It appears not to be as adversely affected by winter and has the potential to become a considerable pest in Australia.

WOLF SPIDERS (*Lycosa* spp.) are common ground-dwelling spiders (below). Usually drab-coloured, with dark brown or black heads, some wolf spiders have lighter markings or an "X" shape on their heads. Wolf spiders are often disturbed in gardens where they burrow in the soil or live among fallen leaves and shrubs. Most bites produce only mild effects, but they can also cause itchiness, red welts, bruising, nausea, localised pain and prolonged headaches among other symptoms.

FAMOUS SPIDERS

The Redback Spider (*Latrodectus hasselti*) is probably Australia's most famous spider. It is found throughout Australia and is common in disturbed, industrial and residential areas.

Female Redback Spiders are black to brown, usually with a bright orange to red stripe on the upper abdomen and an "hourglass" shaped red or orange mark underneath. Juveniles also have white markings on the abdomen.

The Brown Widow Spider (*Latrodectus geometricus*) is a closely related species introduced to north-eastern Australia. This species lacks a red stripe and has a yellow hour-glass pattern on its lower abdomen. It is not as dangerous as the Redback Spider.

Right: **The Redback Spider is the Australian representative of the notorious widow group of spiders found elsewhere in the world.**

TIMID SPIDERS

Black House Spiders (*Badumna insignis*) construct distinctive webs in crevices in tree trunks, among rocks and around homes and buildings. The webs are very lacy with one or more entrances. Black House Spiders are black or very dark grey with an indistinct pale pattern on the abdomen and legs. Their bite may cause severe pain and other unpleasant symptoms. Fortunately, these spiders are timid and retreat deep into their web if disturbed, so bites are rare and usually happen when people are removing the unsightly webs.

Left, top to bottom: **Black House Spiders will build their webs along window/door frames.**

Precautions

Look but never touch. Apply first aid and seek medical attention immediately.

SCORPIONS

Scorpions are distinctive arachnids with a long, sting-bearing tail and a pair of pincers at the front of the body. They are found throughout Australia and some, such as the brown scorpions (*Liocheles* spp.) are common in gardens. Scorpions shelter under logs/rocks and in shallow burrows in earth banks.

Mottled scorpions belong to at least three genera that are all very difficult to identify.

There are also desert species that construct deep spiral burrows in sand. Scorpions are mostly nocturnal, but are sometimes active during the day. Some Australian species have a painful sting, but none are considered dangerous.

If ultra-violet light ("black light") is shone on live or fossil scorpions, they glow or "fluoresce". The fluorescence is caused by an unidentified substance in a very thin outer layer (cuticle) of the scorpion's "body armour" (exoskeleton).

the FACTS!

MOST TICKS are external, bloodsucking parasites of mammals, birds and reptiles. They favour forest, tall grass and shrubby vegetation, where they climb onto plants and wait to jump on a passing host. Ticks can transmit diseases to humans and some are also venomous. The Australian Paralysis, or "Scrub", Tick of eastern Australia produces a paralysing toxin in its salivary glands that can be fatal to small animals and babies. In adults, bites can cause intense itching and sometimes more serious reactions that require hospitalisation.

CENTIPEDES always have an odd number of pairs of legs. The known range is 15–191 pairs.

LONG, LEGGY
ARTHROPODS

Centipedes and millipedes are arthropods (class: Myriapoda, meaning "many pairs of legs"). Centipedes are carnivores and are armed with a pair of fangs containing a poison gland. Bites from large centipedes (such as *Ethmostigmus* spp.) may cause severe pain, swelling and associated complications. The large structures at the rear of a centipede are not stings; they are sensory organs called cerci.

Millipedes feed on plants and decaying vegetable matter, so they have no need for fangs. When threatened, they can release toxins that stain and irritate skin.

Right: The Giant Centipede (*Ethmostigmus rubripes*) is the largest of all Australasian centipedes. The maximum head and body length is around 13.5 cm. Giant Centipedes are powerful predators that can capture and kill small vertebrates, like this small snake. They will also scavenge freshly killed animals on roadways.

QM-JW

Insects
— countless millions

Insects are the most numerous and diverse group of animals on Earth, so it is not surprising to find that their defence mechanisms are as varied as the animals themselves. Some sting, some bite and some cause irritation.

QM

the FACTS!

CUP MOTH CATERPILLARS (above) are known as "Chinese junks", "battleships" or "warships" because of their unusual shape and stinging spines.

IF INHALED, the hairs from processionary caterpillars may cause breathing problems. They can also cause conjunctivitis if they come into contact with the eyes.

VENOMOUS (and poisonous) insects are often brightly patterned in yellow, black and red as a warning to potential predators.

MOST BITES from predatory bugs occur accidentally while gardening or working outside. Some species are attracted to house lights at night and some also shelter in clothing, bedding and shoes.

ITCHY LARVAE

Australian moths and butterflies are beautiful insects and almost all are harmless to humans. However, contact with the larvae (caterpillars) of some can be an unpleasant experience because of their irritating hairs or their venomous spines.

Larvae of the Bag-shelter Moth (*Ochrogaster lunifer*) are known as "processionary caterpillars" because of their habit of forming long, head-to-tail chains as they move between trees. They are also known as "itchy grubs" because their hairs can easily penetrate skin and clothing, causing intense irritation and occasionally severe allergic reactions. Airborne fragments can be inhaled and can also contaminate nearby surfaces such as washing.

Other "itchy" species include tiger moths (family: Arctiidae), gum moths (family: Anthelidae) and tussock moths (family: Lymantriidae).

QM

Mature larvae of Bag-shelter Moths are known as processionary caterpillars.

PREDATORY BUGS

The name "bug" is commonly used to describe any crawling insect, but "true" bugs (order: Hemiptera) all feed on liquid foods that are sucked up through a movable tube (the rostrum) on the underside of the head.

Most species feed on plants, but others, such as assassin bugs and water bugs, are particularly fierce predators. They use the rostrum as a stabbing and piercing weapon and inject their prey with salivary juices that dissolve the animal's internal tissues. The bugs suck up this "soup" and, by the end of the meal, all that is left of the prey is a dry, empty shell.

Bites from large assassin bugs and the Giant Water Bug (*Lethocerus insulanus*) can be extremely painful to humans. Symptoms include an intense burning sensation and sometimes tissue damage around the bite.

QM-JW

Left: The Giant Water Bug is the largest sucking bug in Australia. It preys on tadpoles and small fish.

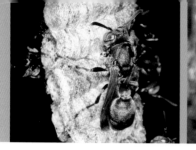

LEFT: QM-JW. RIGHT: IAN MORRIS

Precautions

Look but no not touch. Stay clear of nests. Apply first aid and seek medical attention immediately.

QM-JW

A spider wasp (family: Pompilidae) dragging a spider back to its hole.

the FACTS!

THE GIANT BULL ANT (*Myrmecia brevinoda*), which inhabits rainforest and wet eucalypt forest along the Queensland and New South Wales coast, is one of the longest ants in the world. The largest can be 36 mm long.

HONEY BEES can sting only once, leaving the barbed sting in their victim. The barbs on the sting make it difficult to remove. Most other bees, wasps and ants can sting repeatedly because their stings lack barbs.

AUSTRALIA'S WARM CLIMATE and its lack of natural predators and parasites has helped the European Wasp (*Vespula germanica*) become established in southern parts of the continent. The wasp, which is native to Europe, Asia and North Africa, is often found around houses and in picnic grounds. Wasps will crawl inside soft drink cans — stinging people inside the mouth the next time they take a drink.

PAINFUL STINGS

Wasps, sawflies, ants and bees belong to the insect order Hymenoptera (derived from the Greek words *hymen*, meaning "membrane", and *ptera*, meaning "wings"). Some are "social" and live in colonies, while others are solitary.

Many bees, paper wasps, and several species of ant can all deliver painful stings. Female Hymenoptera usually have a tube-like ovipositor at the end of the abdomen that they may use to deposit eggs. In many bees, ants and some wasps, the ovipositor is a sting that injects venom. Males are stingless.

The venom is ejected at the tip of the sting when it is stabbed into another animal. Ordinarily, bee, wasp and ant stings cause pain and swelling, but for people who have sensitive immune systems, the outcome can be life-threatening.

Social bees, wasps and ants live in colonies and use their stings to repel intruders. People who blunder into paper wasp nests can sustain multiple stings.

The introduced Red Imported Fire Ant is particularly aggressive — workers boil out of the nests and deliver mass stings at the slightest provocation.

IRRITANTS & SMELLS

A number of bloodsucking insects (bedbugs, fleas and biting flies) can cause skin reactions from their saliva or digestive enzymes when they bite.

Some beetles and bugs have toxic defence chemicals that may cause stains, blisters, skin or eye irritation, or smell bad. These include the various "stink bugs", blister beetles (family: Meloidae), whiplash rove beetles (family: Staphylinidae) and "bombardier beetles" (family: Carabidae).

MICHAEL CERMAK

QM-JW

Above: The Green-head Ant (*Rhytidoponera metallica*), has a painful sting.

Left: Blue-banded Bee (*Amegilla* sp.)

QM-JW

STINGS FROM HONEY BEES are the most common cause of allergic reactions in Australia.

Fish
— fearsome spines

More than 50,000 people worldwide are affected by fish venoms every year, with symptoms ranging from pain and blisters to death. Culprits include stingrays, some sharks, lionfish, catfish, scorpionfish, scats, rabbitfish, stargazers and stonefish, to name a few.

the FACTS!

SHARKS ARE A MAJOR predator of rays. Some sharks have been found with stingray spines embedded in the flesh around their mouths. Shark predation may explain why rays react so strongly to large animals that loom above them.

THERE ARE ABOUT 1200 species of fish that can be regarded as venomous, easily making them the most numerous venomous vertebrates.

THE WHISKER-LIKE sensory organs (barbels) around the mouths of catfish are harmless.

THE SCRIBBLED RABBITFISH (*Siganus spinus*) has numerous spines capable of inflicting painful stings, which may endure for some hours. Rabbitfish are often wryly referred to as "happy moments".

JUST DEFENDING THEMSELVES

Rays are generally inoffensive animals that will try to flee if threatened. Stingrays defend themselves by lashing out with their whip-like tails that are usually equipped with one or two, long dagger-like spines. About two-thirds of ray species also have venom glands, hence the name "stingray".

The spines are only erected in times of danger. Anglers, divers and swimmers have been injured and killed when the spines have penetrated vital organs. It is unknown if the fatalities were solely due to the stab wound, or if the venom contributed as well.

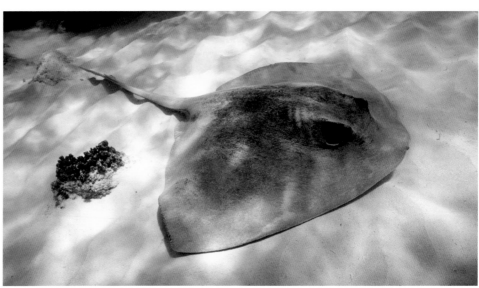

Rays, such as this stingray (*Dasyatis* sp.), are normally placid and content to rest quietly on the bottom. If disturbed, they will "explode" into action and flail their tail as they flee.

STINGING SHARKS

Many small shark species rely on venomous spines as a defence against predators. Dogfish (family: Squalidae), the horn sharks (family: Heterodontidae), elephantfish (family: Callorhinchidae) and chimaeras or ghost sharks (family: Chimaeridae) all have venomous spines on their dorsal (upper) fins. The venom is produced in tissue embedded in a groove along the spine. Stings by some of these sharks are reported to have caused intense localised pain, swelling, numbness and muscle weakness.

Left: Port Jackson Sharks are horn sharks with large blunt heads and distinctive crests over the eyes.

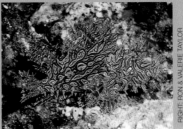

Precautions

Never touch a fish you do not recognise. Be especially careful not to touch spines. Apply first aid and seek medical attention immediately.

BEWARE THE BUTTERFLY

Like insects and other animals, many venomous fish are flamboyant and brightly coloured to warn off predators. Butterfly cod (*Pterois* and *Dendrochirus* spp.), with striped bodies and soft fan-like fins, are among the most beautiful and dangerous of all marine creatures. Butterfly cod, which are also known as lionfish and firefish, have long spines in their dorsal, pelvic and anal fins. Glands located at the base of the spines deliver venom, via the spines, to unwary "attackers". This causes immediate intense pain and other symptoms. Butterfly cod are native to coral and rocky reefs in northern Australian waters and South-East Asian waters. They belong to a group of venomous fish (family: Scorpaenidae), which also includes the less attractive scorpionfish, waspfish and fortesques. The Bullrout (*Notesthes robusta*), is common in estuaries and freshwater in Qld and NSW.

The Common Lionfish (*Pterois volitans*) is dangerously venomous but is very popular with aquarists.

the FACTS!

THE BROWN SABRETOOTH BLENNY (*Petroscirtes lupus*) has venom glands at the base of its fang-like teeth.

CAMOUFLAGED ON THE SEA BED, stonefish wait for small fish and shrimps to swim by before sucking them in with lightning speed. A stonefish ambush has been timed at just 0.015 seconds.

SCORPIONFISH are bottom-dwellers that have spiny, rough or tasselled heads (below, top and centre). All are venomous and should be treated with care.

IT MAY LOOK LIKE A STONE...

Although they are close relatives, stonefish are as ugly as butterfly cod are beautiful. Their warty skin and mottled brown and grey colouring gives almost perfect camouflage among rocks and coral rubble or sand. As slow-moving or motionless bottom-dwellers, they are particularly dangerous to people wading in shallow water.

The Estuarine Stonefish (above) and the Reef Stonefish (right) are regarded as two of the most dangerously venomous marine fish.

Two species occur in Australia — the Reef Stonefish (*Synanceia verrucosa*) and the Estuarine Stonefish, (*Synanceia horrida*). Each has thirteen venomous spines in the dorsal fin along its back and each spine is covered by a sheath that contains venom glands. Downward pressure on the spines (such as standing on them) causes the sheaths to be pushed back and the glands crushed. Venom shoots upward along surface grooves and into the wound.

Excruciating pain, shock and temporary paralysis may follow. There are no recorded deaths from Australia, but the fish is believed to have caused fatalities elsewhere in the Indo-Pacific region.

QM-GC

Snakes
— deadly reptiles

Venomous snakes are probably the most feared animals in the Australian bush. They can be encountered anywhere on the mainland, throughout Tasmania and on many offshore islands. Some can even be found in coastal marine waters.

HOLLOW-FANGED FAMILY

The largest family of Australian snakes is the Elapidae. This family also includes the deadly cobras of Africa and Asia. Elapid snakes have large hollow fangs at the front of their upper jaws. A duct under the skin connects each fang to a venom gland located at the rear of the head. When the snake bites down, muscles squeeze the glands and a stream of venom flows along the duct into the fang.

QM-JW

Young snakes may have bright or distinctive patterns unlike the adults. The distinctive head pattern of this young Eastern Brown Snake (*Pseudonaja textilis*) will be lost as it ages.

the FACTS!

SNAKES DEFEND THEMSELVES by biting, releasing bad odours or feigning death. Other defences include fleeing and camouflage.

IT IS COMMONLY BELIEVED that all snakes are venomous. Many have toxic saliva, but only around 300 of the 2700 known species actually have sophisticated venom-delivery systems.

VENOMOUS SNAKES have the ability to control venom release and many can deliver what is known as a "dry bite".

RESEARCH SUGGESTS that venoms evolved as snakes started to become smaller and more "advanced" around 60 million years ago. The earliest snakes were large, heavy-bodied animals like modern pythons and boas.

STUDIES OF EASTERN BROWN SNAKES have shown that smaller individuals are more likely to flee than larger snakes and that most (77%) give some form of warning display before striking. Researchers also found that 25% of all strikes were a bluff.

GIVEN A BAD NAME

Death adders (*Acanthophis* spp.) are short squat snakes about 50–70 cm long. They have broad heads, small eyes and a tail that ends in a short spine. At least four species occur in Australia, living in all habitats except rainforests. Unlike other elapids, death adders are not active predators, preferring to lie curled and concealed with their tail exposed. The tail is wriggled to lure prey into striking range. **Dangerously venomous.**

The Common Death Adder (*Acanthophis antarcticus*) varies in colour.

STEVE SWANSON

FAR LEFT: QM-BC

Precautions

Do not provoke, handle or attack snakes.
If bitten, seek urgent medical attention.

COPPERHEADS

Despite their common name, none of the copperheads (*Austrelaps* spp.) have a strongly copper-coloured head. These snakes are often found in alpine areas and habitats considered too cold for other snakes. They feed on frogs and skinks, but will also prey on birds and small mammals. When cornered, they will hiss loudly and thrash from side to side. **Dangerously venomous.**

Left: The Highlands Copperhead (*Austrelaps ramsayi*) is the most widespread of the copperheads. It occurs as far north as the New England Tableland of New South Wales.

SMALL-EYED SNAKE

The Eastern Small-eyed Snake (*Cryptophis nigrescens*) of coastal eastern Australia looks like a small Red-bellied Black Snake (*Pseudechis porphyriacus*) because it is black or dark grey above with a reddish or pinkish belly. It occurs in or near forested areas, often close to habitation. It is active at night and preys on snakes, lizards and frogs. **Dangerously venomous.**

The Small-eyed Snake is responsible for one fatality and numerous serious bites.

QM-JW

BLACK WHIPSNAKES

Whipsnakes (*Demansia* spp.) are swift daytime predators of lizards. They have keen eyesight and will pursue prey. The small whipsnakes are not regarded as dangerous, even though bites may cause unpleasant local symptoms. The Greater Black Whipsnake (*Demansia papuensis*) and the Lesser Black Whipsnake (*Demansia vestigiata*) of northern and eastern Australia, should be regarded as potentially dangerous due to their size (more than 1 m).

Left: Black Whipsnake (*Demansia vestigiata*)

QM-BC

the FACTS!

COPPERHEADS (below) occur in temperate, south-eastern Australia and Tasmania. They range in size from the Pygmy Copperhead (*Austrelaps labialis*), which grows to 9 cm, to the Lowlands Copperhead (*A. superbus*), which reaches 1.8 m.

STEVE SWANSON

MOST DEATH ADDERS prefer dry open forests, woodlands, grassland, rocky ranges and deserts, although the Common Death Adder also occurs in shrub and heath.

THERE ARE THREE groups of Australian elapids — the land-dwellers (91 species), the sea snakes (31 species) and sea kraits (two species). The members of all three groups are so closely related that the differences between them are due to their particular lifestyles.

MOST WHIPSNAKE SPECIES are fast-moving, slender snakes with distinctive facial and/or head markings (below).

QM-JW

QM-JW

Snakes
— lethal elapids

STEVE SWANSON

the FACTS!

COLLETT'S SNAKE (*Pseudechis colletti*, above) only occurs on the blacksoil plains of Central Queensland. **Dangerously venomous.**

THE ORNAMENTAL SNAKE (*Denisonia maculata*) is known only from mid-eastern Queensland and the related De Vis' Banded Snake (*Denisonia devisi*) from central Queensland and northern New South Wales. Both are robust, medium-sized snakes (40–60 cm) that feed almost exclusively on frogs. They are secretive and rarely seen, but pugnacious when disturbed. A bite from the Ornamental Snake has caused severe symptoms. **Potentially dangerous.**

BROAD-HEADED SNAKES (*Hoplocephalus* spp.) are medium to large snakes (0.8–1.2 m) that occur in forests, woodlands and rocky areas in eastern Australia. They have broad, flattish patterned heads and faces and plain, speckled or banded bodies. Stephen's Banded Snake (*H. stephensii*, below) is a climbing predator of lizards, birds and small mammals. **Potentially dangerous.**

QM·MT

BLACK SNAKES

Most black snakes (*Pseudechis* spp.) are highly variable in colour. At least eight species of these large (1–2.5 m), powerfully built snakes occur in Australia. The most widespread species is the King Brown (or Mulga) Snake (*P. australis*), which is only absent from high rainfall regions. Along the east coast, the most commonly encountered species is the Red-bellied Black Snake (*P. porphyriacus*). The remaining species have much more restricted distributions. Black snakes prey on frogs, reptiles, birds and mammals. When provoked, they flatten or flare their necks and turn towards the aggressor. **Dangerously venomous.**

LEFT: STEVE SWANSON; RIGHT: QM·JW

The name "black snake" is not appropriate for most *Pseudechis* species. The King Brown Snake varies in colour from rich coppery brown (left) to various shades of olive and slate-grey (right).

THE MOST VENOMOUS SNAKES IN THE WORLD!

The taipans (*Oxyuranus* spp.) are Australia's most dangerous snakes and are among the most venomous snakes in the world. Taipans occur across tropical northern and eastern Australia as well as parts of the inland.

Until recently, it was believed that only two species of taipan occurred in Australia — the Coastal Taipan (*O. scutellatus*) and the Inland Taipan (*O. microlepidotus*). In September 2006, a specimen of a third species (*O. temporalis*) was collected near Walter James Range in Western Australia.

Along with the King Brown Snake, taipans are the largest venomous snakes found in Australia. A mature Coastal Taipan can reach 3 m in length. Taipans mainly feed on mammals, especially rats, and have evolved a "strike and release" strategy and potent, fast-acting venom to deal with animals that can fight back. They are easily provoked and multiple bites are common. **Dangerously venomous.**

Right: The Coastal Taipan occurs across tropical and subtropical coastal regions of northern and eastern Australia. It feeds exclusively on small mammals.

QM·JW

Precautions

Do not provoke, handle or attack snakes. If bitten, seek urgent medical attention.

BROWN SNAKES

Brown snakes are medium to large snakes (0.5–2.2 m) and all but one is regarded as dangerous. The Common Brown Snake (*Pseudonaja textilis*) is common in and near some of the major population centres of eastern Australia, while the Dugite (*P. affinis*) is not uncommon around Perth, Western Australia. The Western Brown Snake (*P. nuchalis*) is the most widespread of the seven species. Brown snakes can be brown or grey to black and olive, or solid coloured, bi-coloured or patterned. All have cream to pale yellow bellies heavily spotted in red or orange. Juvenile brown snakes are more highly coloured than adults. Brown snakes prefer drier country and avoid dense wet forests. They mainly hunt lizards and mammals. These snakes are shy and nervous, but if provoked they will rear up with mouth agape and hold the upper body in an S-shape. Brown snakes will strike rapidly and repeatedly. **Dangerously venomous.**

A threatened Eastern Brown Snake will raise its body in an S-shaped posture, exposing the red or orange spotted belly typical of *Pseudonaja* species.

the FACTS!

COMMON NAMES are often misleading and can contribute to misidentification. Many snakes can only be identified by examining the arrangement and number of body scales.

THE TIGER SNAKE (below) is most abundant in southern Australia, including Bass Strait and islands off the mainland and Tasmanian coasts. Island populations may grow to be unusually large or small depending on the kinds of prey available. Large forms feed on sea birds, especially "muttonbird" chicks.

THE EASTERN BROWN SNAKE has been very successful in adapting to suburban areas of south-eastern Australia. It has the distinction of being the most common dangerous species in areas where the human population is most densely concentrated.

TIGER SNAKES

Many people regard any snake with a banded colour pattern as a "tiger snake". This leads to many harmless species being killed. The "real" Tiger Snake (*Notechis scutatus*) is a large (1–2 m) elapid that can be black, grey or yellow to banded in contrasting shades of light and dark colours. They occur in cool moist parts of eastern and southern Australia and are common on the islands of Bass Strait and Tasmania. Tiger Snakes prey on frogs, lizards, birds and mammals, including the chicks of nesting sea birds. A tiger snake will flatten its body, hiss and turn towards an aggressor when disturbed. **Dangerously venomous.**

Tiger Snakes are common in southern Australia and may be very aggressive when provoked.

Snakes
— fanged hunters

the FACTS!

LARGE SEA SNAKES, such as Stokes' Sea Snake (*Astrotia stokesii*), should be treated with extreme caution, both in the water and when washed-up on a beach.

THE SALIVA of some non-venomous snakes has been reported to cause paralysis of their prey.

THE NON-VENOMOUS Keelback is one of the few natural predators of the introduced Cane Toad. Keelbacks can safely eat small toads and "toadpoles" but will still be poisoned if they eat large toads.

COLUBRIDS PREFER high rainfall areas and rarely extend into semi-arid regions. Elapid snakes are found throughout Australia.

THE SMALLER AUSTRALIAN ELAPID SNAKES (those that grow to less than 1 m long) are often regarded as harmless, but they still deserve to be treated with caution.

MYALL SNAKE

The Myall (or Curl) Snake (*Suta suta*) is another of Australia's dark-headed elapids. Large specimens grow to around 60 cm. Myall Snakes occur in drier, semi-arid and arid areas of eastern Australia and mainly prey on lizards, but also take frogs and mice. When threatened, they curl their body and thrash wildly. Large specimens should be treated with caution. **Dangerously venomous.**

Right: A number of snakes, including the Myall Snake, and snake-like lizards have dark or black heads. The reason for this is unclear.

ROUGH-SCALED SNAKE

The Rough-scaled Snake (*Tropidechis carinatus*) occurs in high rainfall parts and wet forests of eastern Queensland and northern New South Wales. They mainly prey on frogs and small mammals, but will also take birds and lizards. Colour varies from yellowish-brown to olive with irregular dark bands and blotches. Rough-scaled Snakes grow to nearly a metre long and are very unpredictable and quick to bite. **Dangerously venomous.**

STEVE SWANSON

Left: The Rough-scaled Snake is unpredictable. Some individuals can become aggressive with little provocation.

SNAKES & KRAITS OF THE SEA

Sea snakes are elapids that have completely taken to life in marine waters. They are good swimmers because of a paddle-shaped tail and narrow body, but experience great difficulty moving on land. Sea snakes are "live-bearers" that never need to leave the sea to lay eggs. About 30 species have been recorded from Australian waters and most are regarded as dangerously venomous. Sea snakes cannot move on land, but live beach-washed specimens can still bite. Unlike sea snakes, the sea kraits (*Laticauda* spp.) must return to land to lay their eggs. These blue and black banded snakes have a typical snake's body with a paddle-shaped tail. Sea kraits are rare in Australian waters.

RIGHT: RON & VALERIE TAYLOR

Precautions

Do not provoke, handle or attack snakes.
If bitten, seek urgent medical attention.

COLUBRID SNAKES — A DIVERSE FAMILY

Colubrid or solid-toothed snakes are the largest and most diverse family of snakes in the world. On other continents, colubrids dominate the snake fauna, but only 10 species occur in Australia. These are restricted to the wetter tropical areas of the northern and eastern mainland.

VENOMOUS COLUBRIDS produce venom in a large gland (Duvernoy's gland) located near the corner of their jaws. Their "fangs" are little more than a few enlarged, sometimes grooved, teeth located at the rear of the mouth. Venom from the gland simply flows down these teeth to be transferred when the snake bites or chews at its prey — if the teeth are grooved, then the venom can be channelled into the prey. Snakes with grooved rear teeth are better able to channel their venom, but must open their jaws widely to use their "fangs".

The most familiar of all Australian colubrids is unquestionably the elegant and attractive Common Tree Snake (*Dendrelaphis punctulatus*).

STEVE SWANSON

CM

Macleay's Water Snake is one of several rear-fanged water snakes that occur in estuarine or freshwater environments of tropical northern Australia.

REAR-FANGED AUSTRALIAN COLUBRIDS

Five species of rear-fanged colubrid occur in Australia — the Bockadam (*Cerberus australis*), Macleay's Water Snake (*Enhydris polylepis*), White-bellied Mangrove Snake (*Fordonia leucobalia*), Richardson's Sea Snake (*Myron richardsonii*) and Brown Tree Snake (*Boiga irregularis*).

The most widespread of these is the Brown Tree Snake (right), which occurs across northern and eastern Australia as well as New Guinea, Indonesia and nearby islands. The others are rarely encountered aquatic or semi-aquatic snakes of the mangroves or wetlands of the tropical north. None are considered to be dangerously venomous, although bites may produce unpleasant symptoms.

CM-JW

the FACTS!

BROWN TREE SNAKES (below) are nocturnal hunters that prey on birds and small mammals. They will also take frogs and lizards. The Brown Tree Snake is very slender with a large head and protruding eyes. Colour varies from plain light brown to rich reddish-brown with dark or light bands. These snakes are common in bushland, towns and cities and are notorious raiders of caged birds. They are unpredictable and can be easily provoked.

THERE ARE AROUND 1600 species of colubrid snake worldwide and new species are regularly being discovered in remote parts of South America, Asia and Africa.

COLUBRID SNAKES are mainly found in northern and eastern Australia. This suggests that they may have only arrived relatively recently in Australia.

BROWN TREE SNAKES were accidentally introduced among construction materials to the Pacific Island of Guam during World War II. They have since had a devastating impact on the island's wildlife, causing the extinction of nine out of twelve endemic bird species, half of its lizards and possibly some bats.

BROWN TREE SNAKES have grooved rear fangs.

Precautions

Look but do not touch. Platypuses should not be handled. If stung, seek prompt medical attention.

Platypus
— furred stinger

The idea of "cute and cuddly" mammals also being poisonous would surprise most people. In general, mammals rely on their size, powerful limbs, teeth, claws and, in some cases, horns and armour to deter attackers, but a few species of mammals are also venomous.

AUSTRALIA HAS ITS OWN venomous mammal — the Platypus (*Ornithorhynchus anatinus*). Male Platypuses have a spur on the inner side of each hind limb, which is connected to a poison gland by a hollow groove. The spur is used to inflict wounds on natural enemies and on other males during the breeding season. However, it can also cause a painful wound in humans.

the FACTS!

OTHER VENOMOUS MAMMALS include some species of shrew, the rare solenodons (*Solenodon* spp.) from Cuba and Hispaniola and the Slow Loris (*Nycticebus coucang*), a primate from South-East Asia. In most venomous mammals, the venom is produced in modified salivary glands and is transferred when the animal bites.

PLATYPUSES ARE SUPERBLY ADAPTED for their semi-aquatic lifestyle with a duck-like bill, streamlined body and webbed feet. Platypuses swim with alternate strokes of the front feet. The hind feet, which have smaller webs, are mainly for steering and braking while the flat paddle-shaped tail is used as a rudder.

PLATYPUSES BECOME BLIND and deaf when submerged because their eyes, ears and nostrils are closed. The bill is the animal's vital underwater sense organ. It comes equipped with thousands of tiny "sensors", which are sensitive to touch and to the electrical fields generated by other animals.

DAVE WATTS/ANT PHOTO

Wounds from Platypus spurs (left) are rare, but records show they cause excruciating pain that can last for extended periods of time.

A NATURAL TREASURE

The Platypus is one of Australia's greatest natural treasures. An average male Platypus is 50 cm long and weighs 1.7 kg. Females are smaller at about 43 cm and 0.9 kg weight. Platypuses live in freshwater streams, lakes and lagoons all along the east coast of Australia from sea level to the mountains. They have been described as "furred reptiles" or "primitive" mammals because they have a mix of reptile and mammal features. Along with the Echidna (*Tachyglossus aculeatus*), the Platypus belongs to an unique group of animals known as monotremes. The Echidna also has a spur on the hind foot but, unlike the Platypus, it is not venomous.

Natural toxins
— nature's poisons

Precautions
Be aware that natural toxins exist and
where they are likely to be found.

A poisonous animal is one that carries a toxin in its body (or some part of it). These toxins may be produced specifically for defence or simply collected from food or the outside environment. Some toxins only make the animal smell or taste bad, but others can be very harmful to both predators and people.

CANE TOADS (*Bufo marinus*), some crabs, fish and even insects are poisonous. The toxins are usually produced by specialised organs or glands in the body, or in the skin of the animal. They are released when the animal is eaten, bitten or even licked.

Poisonous creatures often "advertise" their danger with bright colours and markings, particularly yellow, black and red. For example, the endangered black and yellow Southern Corroboree Frog (*Pseudophryne corroboree*) of Australia's Alps secretes a deadly toxin in its skin. A predator that ignores "warning colours" risks sickness or death.

the FACTS!

NATURALLY OCCURRING TOXINS can also contaminate food. The most common sources are usually bacteria, moulds, fungi or algae. These may be acquired from organisms living naturally on the food animal, from contact with faeces or decomposing organic matter, or by contact with spores, moulds and airborne material. Most cases of food-poisoning result from these sources rather than the food.

DAMAGED OR MOULDY FOODS (below) are likely to contain toxins. Moulds are usually visible, but their toxins are invisible and can penetrate food. Even if the mould is removed, the toxins may remain. Moulds can grow on most types of food if the conditions are right, but they grow fastest in warm, moist conditions.

The Stars-and-stripes Puffer (*Arothron hispidus*) and many other pufferfish store toxin in their internal organs and sometimes even in their skin.

RECYCLED TOXINS

Plant-eating insects are well-known for their ability to extract, recycle or accumulate the toxins of plants in their own defence. Other groups of animals have similar abilities; for example, some nudibranchs actually modify and use the stinging cells of sea jellies that they eat. Such recycling of toxins may explain how four species of bird from New Guinea have become poisonous. The likely source of their toxins is the insects they eat.

IT IS UNWISE TO BELIEVE that if something is "natural", it must be safe. The botulinum toxin is one of the most deadly toxins known but it is naturally produced by the bacterium *Clostridium botulinum*.

Caterpillars of the Wanderer Butterfly (*Danaus plexippus*) feed on toxic milkweeds. The accumulated toxins are retained by the adult butterflies.

Precautions

Be alert to dangerous substances. Heed all warning signs and advice. Be careful and seek prompt medical attention in the event of poisoning.

Artificial toxins
— the costs of civilisation

the FACTS!

POLLUTANTS THAT ARE STORED in animal body fats may be retained for a long time. Fish and livestock are regularly checked to measure the amount of pollutants in fatty tissues. Milk is routinely tested for pollutants not only because it contains fat, but also because children are often more susceptible to damage from toxins.

IF A POLLUTANT is soluble in water, it is likely to break down and pass through the animal before it causes any harm.

SOME POLLUTANTS become dangerous when they react with other substances in the natural environment. For example, the oxides of nitrogen and sulphur released from the burning of fossil fuels may react with water vapour to cause "acid rain".

Modern civilisation depends on a bewildering array of chemicals used around the home and for industry and agriculture. These chemicals can pass into the environment as "pollutants", affecting wildlife and animals that we use for food.

POLLUTANTS CAN BE ABSORBED directly through the body tissues of an animal. Chemical discharges can have fatal consequences in a very short time, as happens with fish kills in waterways. Chemicals can also be ingested, moving from species to species through the food chain until they reach the animal destined for your dinner plate. Usually, the chemicals become more concentrated at each level of the food chain. For this to occur the chemicals must be long-lived, easily spread, soluble in fat and biologically active, which means they can affect the activity of living cells. At the top of the food chain, the increased concentrations may become toxic, interfere with reproduction of the animal, or cause diseases such as cancer.

Waterways and coastal waters have often been used for the deliberate disposal of wastes. Run-off can also add other forms of contamination. River flows and coastal currents can then carry these contaminants to threaten coastal fisheries and shellfish farms.

HUMAN HEALTH

Pollutants pose a number of threats to human health, especially through food. The mobility of some pollutants means that livestock and fisheries may be contaminated, even though they may lie at some distance from the pollution source.

Fisheries are especially vulnerable to pollution and numerous serious cases of poisoning, caused by high mercury levels in fish and shellfish, have been recorded worldwide. One of the most tragic events of this type occurred at Minamata Bay in Japan in 1953. In this case, 111 people were affected by eating fish that contained high levels of mercury and 43 villagers died.

Warning

Radioactive

Toxic

Biohazard

Dangerous substances need to be labelled to identify the type of risk.

Molluscs
— toxins & taints

Bivalve molluscs, such as mussels, clams, oysters and scallops, are an important part of Australia's commercial and recreational fisheries. As filter-feeders that take nutrients from the water, they are especially vulnerable to pollutants. Oysters and mussels can accumulate various bacteria, toxins and pollutants in their tissues.

Above: Oysters and mussels can be seasonally toxic following flows of water contaminated by the faecal bacteria, *Escherichia coli*, or following "blooms" of microscopic dinoflagellates. It is not possible to identify contaminated wild oysters just by looking at them, so never assume that they are safe to eat.

Below: Mussels are a common and distinctive component on almost every rocky shore. Large species are harvested commercially.

IT HAS BEEN KNOWN FOR HUNDREDS OF YEARS that eating "shellfish" (as molluscs are sometimes called) can occasionally be dangerous. Shellfish poisoning can be due to viruses, bacteria or pollutants, but most often results from the animals becoming infected during "blooms" of toxic dinoflagellates. These are microscopic, single-celled organisms that occur naturally in seawater and are frequently associated with algae.

Contaminated shellfish can cause a range of symptoms from mild allergic reactions to severe illness and, in some cases, death. The toxins responsible for shellfish poisoning are water-soluble, but they remain stable if heated or placed in acids. This means that the toxins are not deactivated by ordinary cooking methods or digestive juices. Some are less toxic, but have the ability to taint the molluscs, rendering them unpalatable.

the FACTS!

POPULATION EXPLOSIONS (or "blooms") of dinoflagellates usually occur after changes in water temperature and flow, or with increased nutrient levels. Most blooms are harmless and only colour the water, leading to the phenomenon known as "red tides". Blooms of toxic species can have a serious impact on marine life. Shellfish from areas affected by "red tides" should not be eaten.

AT LEAST FOUR DISTINCT TYPES of shellfish poisoning occur and each is due to a specific group of toxins. Paralytic shellfish poisoning (PSP) is probably the best known type of shellfish poisonings, with more than 100 known deaths around worldwide.

SOME SEA SCALLOP SPECIES form the basis of a multi-million dollar industry in Australia. The majority of species, like this Leopard Scallop (*Annachlamys flabellata*), are not commercially harvested.

IN 1987 IN PORT PHILLIP BAY, Melbourne, a bloom of another microscopic organism, called a diatom, caused local shellfish to develop a powerful bitter taint. This was so persistent and unpleasant the shellfish could not be sold for almost a year — costing the industry about $1 million.

Crustaceans
— off the menu

Crabs are the best known group of crustaceans. They have a great diversity of shape, size and colour, but always have one pair of chelipeds ("claws", "pincers" or "nippers") and four pairs of walking legs. Crabs are generally, but not always, wider than they are long and are able to walk sideways.

IN AUSTRALIA, THE MUD CRAB (*Scylla serrata*) is a popular "table" species and crabs are an important food source for people around the world. Most species of crab are edible, but some are highly toxic and are known to have caused fatalities, especially in the Asia-Pacific region.

The most common offenders are the brightly coloured, black-fingered reef crabs (family: Xanthidae), so named for the black or dark brown movable "fingers" on each cheliped. Some of these crabs are bright red or highly patterned, but others are inconspicuous.

the FACTS!

MOST TOXIC CRABS are omnivores that feed on large food items. It is suspected that bacteria and algae are the source of toxins. It is not known why some crabs carry enormous amounts of toxin.

THE MAIN TOXINS carried by poisonous crabs carry several toxins including saxitoxin and other paralytic shellfish poisoning (PSP) toxins, in addition to palytoxin and tetrodotoxin. Some of these, especially saxitoxin and PSP toxins, may be acquired via the food chain.

THE BOXER CRAB (*Lybia tesselata*) carries a pair of small anemones in its nippers (chelipeds). When approached by a predator it waves these around, presenting the stinging tentacles so as to deter the marauder. The anemones benefit from the small particles of food dropped by the crab during feeding.

ONE SPECIES OF SHAWL CRAB, *Atergatis floridus*, which grows to around 12.5 cm, is known to have caused numerous poisonings across the Indo-Pacific region.

Many different species of crab live along Australia's coastline. Most species, like the Variegated Shore Crab (*Leptograpsus variegatus*), are quite edible but too small to be of commercial value.

LARGEST GROUP

Black-fingered crabs are one of the largest groups of crabs in Australian waters (around 160 species). Only a small number of species are toxic and there have not been any serious cases of poisoning in Australia.

Toxicity levels vary in individual crabs, as do the types of toxins. This may be linked to the foods the crabs eat. Some feed by scraping algae, while others are aggressive predators. A few live in mutually beneficial (symbiotic) relationships with corals, sea anemones and other cnidarians.

Precautions

Never eat small reef crabs. Seek medical attention urgently if poisoning is suspected.

An East Timorese man died within several hours of eating Devil Crabs in 2000. His death highlighted the danger of eating tropical crabs.

"BLUE" DEVILS

The Devil Crab (*Zosimus aeneus*) is regarded as one of the most poisonous of all crustaceans. It is claimed that as little as half a gram of flesh from one of its claws is sufficient to kill a human. Unlike other species of black-fingered crabs, the shell of the Devil Crab is mainly blue with black, pale-edged spots. The crab grows to 15 cm and occurs on rocky and coral reefs across the Indian and Pacific Oceans.

CHANGE OF COLOUR

Other toxic black-fingered crabs include the Brown Shawl Crab (*Atergatis integerrimus*), which grows to 17.5 cm, and Splendid Reef Crab (*Etisus splendidus*), which grows to 30 cm. Both species have bright red shells.

Some species of black-fingered crab display more variation. In shawl crabs (*Atergatis* spp.) colours and patterns change from dark red with clusters of dark-edged, creamish blotches around the edges to mainly brown with a pale lacy pattern or stain on the back.

The Blood-spotted Crab (*Carpilius maculatus*) is light brown with few large red spots. The red and white painted crabs (*Lophozozymus* spp.) grow to 20 cm and are mostly red, but are also densely covered in tiny white spots.

Black-fingered crabs are not the only poisonous species. Sixteen other species are known to have toxic flesh. These include a type of elbow crab (*Daldorfia horrida*), some swimming crabs (*Thalamita* spp.), spider crabs (*Schizophrys aspera*), shore crabs (*Grapsus* and *Percnon* spp.) and the Common Box Crab (*Calappa calappa*).

The Convex Reef Crab (*Carpilius convexus*) is often found in the same habitats as black-fingered crabs. Any small reef crab is potentially toxic.

Box crabs (*Calappa* spp.) inhabit rocky and coral reefs and sandy or muddy bottoms.

the FACTS!

AN INDIVIDUAL DEVIL CRAB reportedly can contain enough toxin in its body to kill hundreds, if not thousands, of people. It is estimated that 65–100% of all Devil Crabs are toxic.

THE HERMIT CRAB (*Dardanus deformis*), which is found on the Great Barrier Reef, has a symbiotic relationship with the stinging sea anemone *Calliactis polypus*. The anemone attaches to the crab's shell and provides camouflage and protection. The two animals also share food. As the crab moves, it helps the anemone to disperse. When the crab outgrows its shell, it either transfers the anemone to the new shell or finds a larger anemone.

HERMIT CRABS differ from other crabs because their abdomen is not covered by an exoskeleton, but is soft and delicate. For protection, they use discarded snail shells. As hermit crabs grow and their current shell becomes too small, they must go in search of another one. The crab pictured below has made a home from a cone shell.

Pufferfish
— a fatal family

Poisonous pufferfish, toadfish and their relatives are regarded as pests by Australian anglers. Incredibly, in some parts of the world, these fish are considered a food delicacy, not a health hazard.

the FACTS!

TETRAODONTIFORMES are not related to any other group of fish. They have two pairs of large teeth at the front of the jaws, which are often visible even when the mouth is closed. They also have tiny gill slits that lack a covering flap, usually a single rear dorsal fin, a large anal fin and no pelvic fins.

ABOUT 100 PEOPLE DIE each year after eating pufferfish.

SUNFISH (below) can weigh more than 2000 kg and grow to more than 3 m. Despite their size, sunfish are harmless to people. They feed on sea jellies, other soft-bodied marine creatures and occasionally small crustaceans and fish. The mouth of a sunfish is very small in comparison to the size of its body and the teeth in each jaw are fused together to from a single plate.

MARK CONLIN/MARINE THEMES

THERE ARE ABOUT 130 pufferfish and globefish species. Most species are small but some reach 90 cm in length. Pufferfish occur in the tropical and subtropical parts of the Atlantic, Indian and Pacific Oceans. They prefer to stay near the bottom where they can feed on molluscs and crustaceans.

THE POISON THAT THESE FISH CARRY in their tissues is known as tetrodotoxin and some scientists believe it to be more deadly than cyanide. In Japan, the flesh is eaten raw and is known as *fugu*. Specially trained chefs remove the internal organs of a fish, where the poison is most concentrated; however, it is not uncommon for diners to die from respiratory paralysis. The toxin is prevalent in some species and unknown in others.

Boxfish, like this Eastern Smooth Boxfish (*Anoplocapros inermis*), are found mainly on tropical and subtropical reefs.

A BIZARRE GROUP

Pufferfish belong to a large order of strange-looking fish known as Tetraodontiformes. The group of 360 species includes leatherjackets, triggerfish, porcupinefish, boxfish, trunkfish, toadfish, spikefish and the gigantic Ocean Sunfish.

These fish have bizarre body shapes and many have other defence mechanisms besides poison. When threatened, some species are able to inflate their bodies so that they resemble pincushions. Others look like armoured boxes or metal files and have sharp spikes and spines.

Most Tetraodontiformes inhabit shallow tropical and temperate seas, but some enter brackish or freshwater habitats.

Starry Puffer (*Arothron stellatus*)

Precautions

Do not eat any pufferfish or related species.
If caught, release immediately. Handle with care.

TOADFISH

Toadfish are often seen in very
shallow water along beaches and
near estuaries. The Common Toadfish
(*Tetractenos hamiltoni*, above) is known
to be poisonous and is one of the few
fish that allows itself to be stranded
on sandy flats with the receding tide.
Toadfish use their pectoral fins to make
a shallow "nest" while waiting for the
rising tide to carry them back.

PUFFERS

Pufferfish are so named because
they can "puff" themselves up into
a spherical "ball" when threatened.
A pufferfish, like the Narrowlined Puffer
(*Arothron manilensis*, above) does this
by gulping water until its stomach is
full, causing it to swell in size. When
the threat has passed, the water is
released and the puffer returns to its
normal shape and size.

BOXFISH

Boxfish cannot inflate, but rely on
"armour" for defence. Their scales are
fused together, making a solid "box"
shape from which the fins and tail
protrude. Tropical boxfish have squarer
bodies than species found in temperate
waters. Cowfish are found in the tropics
and are named for the "horns" that
project from in front of their eyes.

Left: Yellow Boxfish (*Ostracion cubicus*)

PORCUPINEFISH

The porcupinefish, which is also known as the burrfish
and globefish, gets its name from the numerous long
spines located all over its head and body. Usually
the spines lay flat but, when threatened, the fish
expands its body and erects the spines. When fully
inflated, the fish has a formidable presence, which
makes predators think twice about taking a bite.

Right: Spotted Porcupinefish (*Diodon hystrix*)

the FACTS!

THE SMOOTH TOADFISH
(*Tetractenos glaber*) is another
common Australian species. It is
pale greenish with black blotches
on the back and sides. Unlike the
similar Common Toadfish, it is
smooth-skinned and may also grow
larger (150 mm).

**SOME TRIGGERFISH BECOME
AGGRESSIVE** during the breeding
season and will bite divers and other
intruders if they venture too close to
nesting sites.

THE SILVER TOADFISH
(*Lagocephalus sceleratus*),
also known as the Giant or
Silver-cheeked Toadfish, grows to
90 cm. It is an aggressive species
that is famous for biting the feet and
hands of swimmers and divers. The
powerful jaws of the Silver Toadfish
are strong enough to shear through
the shanks of hooks and even bone.

TIGER SHARKS eat venomous and
poisonous prey, including pufferfish.
It is not known how the sharks
survive such seemingly inedible
and poisonous prey.

UNQUESTIONABLY, the most
dangerous Australian pufferfish is
the Ferocious Puffer (*Feroxodon
multistriatus*). Not only is this fish
poisonous, it is highly aggressive
and will make unprovoked attacks
on people even in shallow water. It
has been known to bite off the toes
of some of its victims.

**BOXFISH CANNOT
BE KEPT IN
AQUARIUMS**
because their
toxic skin
secretions will
kill other fish.

IAN MORRIS

Frogs
— handle with care

Frogs often look vulnerable because they lack sharp teeth, beaks or claws. This doesn't mean they are defenceless. Frogs have many ways to avoid danger. They usually leap to safety or use camouflage colours to hide. Some frogs even produce poisonous skin secretions.

the FACTS!

AUSTRALIA'S NATIVE FROGS range from tiny "froglets" and "toadlets" about 2 cm long to large tree-frogs and barred frogs that grow to 11–11.5 cm.

ONE OF THE MOST COMMON ways frogs avoid danger is to remain very still and so escape notice. Many frogs also have "flash" colours on the backs of their legs, groin and "armpit". When the frog leaps to escape, the bright colours distract the predator. If they are caught, some frogs are able to make a loud noise to scare off the predator.

THE DEADLIEST FROG in the world is the poison dart frog, (*Phyllobates terribilis*) from Central and South America. One specimen may contain up to 1900 micrograms of toxins in its skin glands — enough to kill a human if it entered an open wound or was ingested.

EMERALD-SPOTTED TREE-FROGS (*Litoria peronii*) have toxic skin secretions that may cause their distinctive musty smell.

SKIN SECRETIONS are a complex mixture of different chemical compounds and are used to deter a range of organisms from microscopic bacteria to major predators (such as snakes and birds). The compounds are produced in numerous glands in the skin and may cause an unpleasant taste or have more serious consequences for a would-be predator.

QM

The Black Soled Frog (*Lechriodus fletcheri*) inhabits rainforests and wet eucalypt forests of South-East Queensland and northern New South Wales. It has a powerful skin toxin.

SKIN PROTECTION

Fortunately, none of Australia's 220 native frog species are dangerous to humans, but their skin secretions may cause irritation or burning upon contact with the skin or eyes. Similarly, oils, soap, perspiration and other chemicals on human hands may harm the very sensitive skin of frogs.

Toxic frogs are often brightly coloured in red, yellow, orange or blue, such as the corroboree frogs (*Pseudophryne* spp.) of the Australian Alps.

The Southern Corroboree Frog (*Pseudophryne corroboree*) is one of Australia's most striking frogs.

HELP KEEP WA FREE OF CANE TOADS

HAVE YOU CHECKED YOUR VEHICLE & GEAR ?
To report suspected sightings in WA or dispose of a cane toad found in your vehicle or gear freecall 1800 084 881

Precautions

Never touch, provoke or torment Cane Toads.
Handle native frogs with care.

The breeding call of a male Cane Toad is stuttering and sounds like a portable generator.

BIG MISTAKE!

The poisonous Cane Toad (*Bufo marinus*) is one of Australia's worst environmental pests. It was released into the cane fields of Far North Queensland in 1935 in an attempt to control two serious insect pests — Grey-back (*Dermolepida albohirtum*) and Frenchi Beetles (*Lepidiota frenchi*). The toad proved useless at controlling the beetles, but found the warm wet tropical conditions to its liking. Since then, the toad has spread over most of northern Australia and is a major threat to native wildlife.

the FACTS!

THE CANE TOAD is native to Central and South America. It is also known as the Giant American or Marine Toad.

THE CANE TOAD IS TOXIC at all stages of its life and care should be taken when handling adults or large numbers of tadpoles and eggs. Wash hands thoroughly after touching a toad.

SOME NATIVE ANIMALS, notably the Water-rat (*Hydromys chrysogaster*), Torresian Crow (*Corvus orru*) and the Keelback (*Tropidonophis mairii*), have learned to prey on toads. They do this by either avoiding the toxic skin glands, or by feeding on tadpoles and juvenile toads.

CANE TOAD EGGS are laid in long continuous strands or chains, often entangled with submerged vegetation or debris.

"TOADPOLES" SWIM AND FEED in schools and also form dense aggregations ("mats") on the bottom of shallow water bodies (left).

MILKY TOXINS

Cane Toads have skin glands that produce a thick milky secretion when the animal is under threat. This secretion is a cocktail of toxins that prove deadly to other animals. Most of the toxins are secreted by the swollen neck (parotid) glands with lesser amounts from the skin on the back. It is not uncommon for native animals and family pets to die after they have tried to bite or eat toads. In the wild, toads compete for food, shelter and breeding sites with native animals.

Keelbacks can safely eat small toads and "toadpoles" but are likely to be killed when eating a specimen of this size. In most cases, the snake will die before fully consuming the toad.

It is not surprising the Cane Toad became a pest. Toads are prolific breeders — some estimates suggest that a female can lay up to 40,000 eggs in a single breeding season. They do not require specialised diets or breeding conditions and they are able to tolerate a wide range of habitats.

Left: A group of male Cane Toads gathering at a breeding pool. Female Cane Toads are much more secretive.

Turtles
— threatened delicacy

the FACTS!

RESEARCHERS are working to collect information that may help save turtles from extinction.

THE PRINCIPAL CAUSE of the worldwide decline of marine turtles is the continuing harvest of eggs and adults in their nesting beaches and of juveniles and adults in feeding grounds. Incidental capture in fishing gear (gillnets, trawls, traps, pots, longlines and dredges) and collisions with boats also cause many fatalities. In some parts of the world, turtles are also threatened by disease.

TURTLES ARE OF GREAT CULTURAL, spiritual and economic importance to Indigenous Australians who live in coastal regions. Turtles feature in many Indigenous stories, ceremonies and traditions.

MARINE TURTLES LOOK as though they are "crying" when on land. Their tears are a concentrated salt solution that removes excess salt from their bodies through a gland near their eyes.

TURTLES HAVE AN ACUTE SENSE OF SMELL, well-developed eyes with good colour vision, but a poor sense of taste. They mainly hear low frequency sounds.

Marine turtles have existed for more than 100 million years and they are an important part of Australia's marine ecosystems. Six species of large marine turtle are found in the continent's northern waters.

MARINE TURTLES have long been exploited for food. Turtle soup was an extremely popular item on the dinner menus of European restaurants and homes until the early 20th century. There was even a turtle fishery and turtle-canning factories operated along Australia's northern coastline.

This industry mainly relied on the capture of adult female Green Turtles at their nesting beaches. It is doubtful that turtle harvesting was sustainable in the long term because of its impact on breeding populations. However, the industry was destroyed by a number of food-poisoning scandals elsewhere in the world during the early 20th century. Canned turtle products were blamed for the outbreaks.

Below: Marine turtles, like this Green Turtle, are an important food resource for coastal Indigenous communities.

DEADLY FOOD

Poisoning outbreaks and fatalities from eating turtles and their eggs are still regularly recorded worldwide. The flesh of sea turtles can contain bacteria and natural toxins and can accumulate pollutants. One of the main causes of turtle poisoning, chelonitoxin, is acquired via the food chain. Turtle poisoning is said to cause nausea, vomiting, diarrhoea, a burning sensation in the lips, tongue and mouth, chest tightness, difficulty swallowing, hypersalivation and sometimes death.

Left and inset: Freshwater turtles are sometimes called "tortoises". They are closely related to the marine turtles, so it is appropriate to call them "turtles" too.

CHELONITOXIN HAS BEEN FOUND mainly in the Hawksbill Turtle (*Eretmochelys imbricata*), but it is also known to occur in Green Turtles (*Chelonia mydas*) and Leatherbacks (*Dermochelys coriacea*). All three species are found in Australian waters.

HAWKSBILL TURTLE

The Hawksbill Turtle takes its name from its beak-like mouth and narrow head. The Hawksbill favours coral and rocky reefs in tropical and subtropical areas. Sponges make up a major part of the turtle's diet, although they also feed on algae, sea cucumbers, soft corals and shellfish.

The jaws are well adapted to prising food from crevices in and around coral. Hawksbills have attractively patterned shells. "Tortoiseshell" was widely used until the 1970s in the manufacture of combs, eyewear and guitar picks.

GREEN TURTLE

Green Turtles are the largest of all the hard-shelled sea turtles. Adults can weigh 135–160 kg. They are herbivorous, feeding primarily on seagrasses and algae. This diet is thought to give them the greenish coloured fat from which they take their common name.

A Green Turtle's upper carapace (shell) is smooth and can be shades of black, grey, green, brown and yellow. The underside of the carapace is usually whitish.

LEATHERBACK TURTLE

The Leatherback Turtle has a shell that looks like a dark, upturned dinghy. The shell consists of numerous small bones that lie beneath its leathery skin. It has seven pronounced ridges on its back and five on the underside.

Leatherbacks are the largest of the marine turtles and can reach enormous sizes. The heaviest individual ever recorded weighed 916 kg. Leatherbacks feed in the open ocean and eat sea jellies.

Hawksbill Turtle (*Eretmochelys imbricata*)

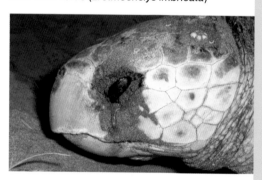

Green Turtle (*Chelonia mydas*)

RON & VALERIE TAYLOR

Leatherback Turtle (*Dermochelys coriacea*)

the FACTS!

TURTLES ARE AIR BREATHERS that must come to the surface regularly, but they can adjust their metabolism to stay underwater for long periods of time. Unlike most other reptiles, marine turtles and their freshwater relatives have hardened jaw sheaths rather than teeth to tear, crush and crop their prey.

SEA TURTLES BECOME SEXUALLY mature at 30–50 years and can live for up to 100 years. They lay their eggs in sand and the temperature of the sand determines the sex of the young turtles. Cooler sand produces male turtles, while warmer sand produces females. Sea turtles can lay up to 100 eggs.

TURTLE HATCHLINGS are carried out to sea on ocean currents and travel thousands of kilometres before they are fully grown. Mature adults return to the same areas where they hatched to lay their own eggs.

ADULT MARINE TURTLES are migratory. Each year they travel between the same feeding grounds and breeding areas.

Precautions

Good personal hygiene is critical, especially thorough hand washing. Follow medical advice when ill.

Micro-organisms
— the unseen world

Human beings can contract diseases from other people or from other animals. Disease-causing agents are known as "pathogens" and together they can attack almost any part of the body, from the surface of the skin to internal organs.

PATHOGENS INCLUDE VIRUSES, bacteria, protozoa, parasites and fungi. Some diseases affect only people. Pathogens that cause disease in both animals and humans are known as "zoonoses". Fortunately, zoonotic disease is not common and can often be prevented if precautions are taken.

the FACTS!

FUNGI ARE SINGLE- OR MULTI-CELLED ORGANISMS that include yeasts, moulds (below) and mildews. Many fungus species grow as a web-like structure (mycelium) made up of many strands (hyphae). The mycelium is sometimes visible but it often grows in soil or inside organic matter, plants or animals. Mushrooms and puffballs are fungi but they are the reproductive "fruiting bodies" of particular species.

THE LARGEST KNOWN SINGLE ORGANISM on Earth is a fungus. An individual *Armillaria ostoyae* (a "honey mushroom") growing in western Washington State in the United States covers nearly 9 km² and weighs perhaps 3600 tons. It may be about 2400 years old. An individual *Armillaria bulbosa* growing in northern Michigan covers only 0.2 km², but is thought to be 10,000 years old. This would make it the oldest known living organism on the planet.

VIRUSES

Viruses are unlike any other organism and for many years scientists debated if they were actually "living things". Viruses can only replicate by infecting a host cell. They cannot reproduce on their own. Viruses can infect plants, animals, fungi and even other micro-organisms. They are extremely tiny and can only be viewed individually using powerful electron microscopes.

Right: Viruses cause a wide variety of human ailments. Dengue (DF) and dengue hemorrhagic fever (DHF) are caused by a group of four closely related viruses.

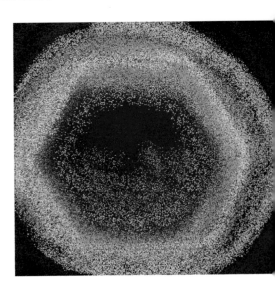

PROTOZOA & SIMILAR ORGANISMS

Protozoa are also single-celled organisms. They are sometimes regarded as either animals (in that they move and obtain food from their environment) or plants (if they have structures that contain chlorophyll). Protozoa are important parasites and pathogens and can cause serious diseases like malaria.

BACTERIA

Bacteria are single-celled micro-organisms and they are found everywhere on Earth. They grow in soil, hot acidic water, radioactive waste, seawater and even deep in the Earth's crust. While some are harmful, others are vital for recycling nutrients in the environment and for maintaining the health of animals and plants.

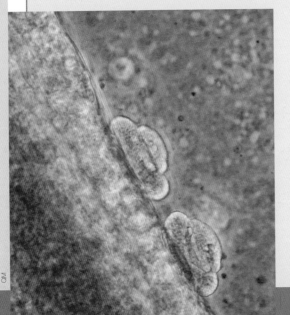

Parasitic protozoans (*Trichodina* spp.) on the edge of a gill filament of a fish.

Parasites
— hunting for hosts

A parasite is an organism that lives in, or on, another plant or animal and obtains its nourishment or some form of life support from the host organism. Depending on the relationship with its host, a parasite may cause little harm, but always benefits at the expense of the host.

PARASITES THAT LIVE INSIDE THE BODY OF A HOST are called endoparasites. The intestinal worms that can affect both humans and animals are examples of endoparasites. When a parasite lives on the outside of a host's body it is called an ectoparasite. Fleas and some mites are ectoparasites. There are even parasites that feed on other parasites and these are known as epiparasites.

Tapeworms of the genus *Calliobothrium* live in the gut of vertebrates. The head (scolex) is armed with hooks that allow the worms to grip the walls of the host's intestine.

1 mm

DIFFERENT LIVES

The relationship between a parasite and its host can be very simple or extremely complicated. Many internal parasites enter their host through their body tissues (e.g. through cuts or insect bites). At other times, the parasites are ingested through certain foods. External parasites are often bloodsuckers that are present just long enough to take a meal from the host. Some ectoparasites have elaborate ways of finding hosts, using movement, temperature and chemical detection, while others simply wait in "ambush" for a passing host. Parasites use tiny hooks, sucking mouthparts or claws to attach themselves to their hosts.

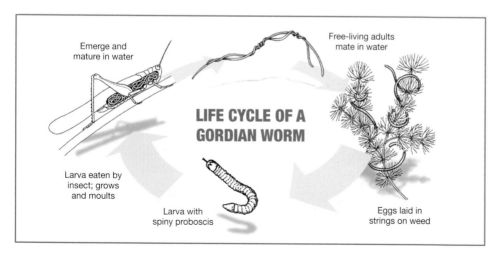

Emerge and mature in water

Free-living adults mate in water

LIFE CYCLE OF A GORDIAN WORM

Larva eaten by insect; grows and moults

Larva with spiny proboscis

Eggs laid in strings on weed

Above: Gordian worms are parasites of insects and spiders, but do not spend their whole life cycle within the host. These worms are completely harmless to humans and other animals.
Right: Gordian worm emerging from a cricket.

the FACTS!

BACTERIA ARE TYPICALLY a few micrometres long and are shaped like curved rods, spheres and spirals.

BACTERIA CAN CAUSE DISEASE in animals and humans, but certain bacteria are used to produce the antibiotics that fight infection.

THE NAME "PARASITE" is derived from the Greek word *parasitos* — "to eat at another's table".

PARASITES AFFECT HUMANS as well as our pets and animals.

THE DIFFERENCE BETWEEN a predator and a parasite is a matter of timing. Predators are only in contact with prey long enough to obtain a meal, while a parasite is dependent on its host for much of its life. Animals such as leeches and mosquitoes, may be more correctly called "micropredators" rather than ectoparasites.

PARASITES ARE FOUND EVERYWHERE and about 50% of all animals are parasites. Every healthy ecosystem is riddled with parasites and they may well be necessary for the proper functioning of any given ecosystem.

Vectors & hosts
— agents of disease

the FACTS!

SALMONELLA BACTERIA live in the intestinal tract of many types of animals, including livestock, poultry and reptiles. The bacteria are released in the faeces of these animals, particularly during periods of stress, such as when the animals are yarded and transported (below). Other animals and humans can ingest *Salmonella* bacteria through direct or indirect contact with faeces. The resulting infection, a form of gastroenteritis, can be debilitating, especially in young children and the elderly.

ESCHERICHIA COLI is a bacterium that occurs normally in cattle, sheep, goats, pets and wild birds. People who become infected by these bacteria suffer a range of health problems from diarrhoea to kidney failure. Fatalities have also been reported. Good personal hygiene, particularly after contact with animal faeces, is critical — it takes only a few bacteria to cause human infection.

Molluscs (snails, "sea shells", oysters, mussels, squids and their relatives) are important food sources and are also collected for their beauty so there is a high level of human contact with these animals.

MOST MOLLUSCS ARE HARMLESS, a few are venomous and some carry disease and parasites. Filter-feeding molluscs, such as oysters and clams, do not digest all the organisms that they filter from the surrounding water. As a result, live bacteria and viruses may collect in the tissues of "shellfish" and cause infections in the animals that eat them (including humans). Some of these bacteria and viruses occur naturally and others come from sewage and organic wastes dumped in waterways.

One of the consequences of rapid population growth in coastal regions of Australia is a rise in the levels of bacteria, such as *Salmonella* species and *Escherichia coli* in surrounding waters. These bacteria come from human and animal wastes and unacceptably high levels of them are frequently found in local oysters, mussels and clams. This can lead to the closure of commercial farming in affected areas.

Coastal regions of Australia have been intensively developed for towns, cities, industry and agriculture. Such development may have unintended consequences for human health.

RISKY WILD OYSTERS

Contaminated oysters cause food-poisoning and other gastrointestinal illnesses in humans. It is most prevalent in people who have been collecting and eating raw oysters because cooking destroys most of the common pathogens.

One of the worst cases of food poisoning in Australia occurred in 1978 when around 2000 people in four states were infected by oysters farmed in the Georges River near Sydney. The source of the infection was a *Vibrio* bacterium — the same genus of bacteria responsible for the cholera disease. Strict standards of testing, purification and handling were introduced following this outbreak, ensuring that farmed oysters are a clean food.

Right: Harvesting shellfish can be a pleasant but sometimes risky pastime.

Precautions

Never eat shellfish, drink untreated water or swim close to potential sources of contamination. Heed warning signs. Wash hands thoroughly. Seek medical advice if symptoms appear.

MOLLUSCS & PARASITES

Molluscs may be intermediate hosts for a number of parasitic worms that pose minor to serious health risks to humans. In some cases, the worm's eventual interaction with humans is part of its normal lifecycle. In other cases, the parasite–human relationship is one of "convenience", with people simply being in the wrong place at the wrong time.

Freshwater snails are intermediate hosts for the Asian or Oriental Blood Fluke (*Schistosoma japonicum*), which can lead to a serious disease called schistosomiasis (or bilharzia). The worm develops inside a snail and is then passed into freshwater. People who come into contact with the water through swimming, drinking or any other activity become infected when the worm penetrates their skin. About 200 million people around the world suffer from bilharzia. Fortunately, the Oriental Blood Fluke does not occur in Australia, but there are several related species of liver flukes (*Fasciola* spp.), carried by snails, which are capable of causing infection.

The Green Pond-snail (*Austropeplea viridis*) is an intermediate host for the Common Liver Fluke (*Fasciola hepatica*).

the FACTS!

AQUATIC SNAILS are herbivores that feed on water weeds, rotting vegetation and algae. They can be found clinging to rocks, logs or water plants.

THE STRIATED POND-SNAIL (*Pseudosuccinea columella*, top right) is an intermediate host for the liver fluke.

APPLE SNAILS (*Pomacea* spp.) are imported freshwater snails that are commonly sold in the aquarium trade (below). These attractive snails are native to South America. Some species pose a potentially serious biological threat to Australian waterways if they are ever allowed to escape. It is also possible that these snails could carry parasites and diseases.

AUSTRALIA HAS ABOUT 170 SPECIES of freshwater snail, and just over 30 species of freshwater mussel or clam. They inhabit freshwater to brackish rivers, streams, lakes, ponds, swamps and dams.

BATHER'S ITCH

"Bather's itch" is an unpleasant, intensely itchy rash that is usually contracted on the New South Wales coast and often blamed on "sea lice". The real culprits are the misguided larvae of the parasitic flatworm, *Austrobilharzia terrigalensis*. The flatworms are actually a parasite of birds that use the mudwhelk (or mudcreeper), *Velacumantus australis*, as an intermediate host. After leaving the whelk, the larvae drift near the surface of tidal lagoons and shallow inlets. They are able to penetrate human skin, but cannot enter the body's bloodstream because humans are the "wrong" host. The larvae die and the rash, which may form raised itchy lumps or pimples, is caused by an allergic reaction to these invaders.

Mud whelks and related species are a common sight in shallow waters on tidal mudflats and among mangroves.

Insects
— more than a nuisance

the FACTS!

THERE ARE TWO LICE that attack humans. The Head Louse (*Pediculus humanus capitus*) feeds on the scalp and *Phthirus pubis* in the groin and armpits. Infestations result in itchy, irritated skin and the lice are spread by close contact or shared clothing.

BUBONIC PLAGUE caused 165 deaths in 1900 when it first appeared in Australia. The disease remained active for 10 years and a total of 1212 cases of infection were reported with 530 fatalities. Most infections were recorded in Sydney and others occurred in New South Wales, Victoria, Queensland, Western Australia and the Northern Territory. Professional rat-catchers (below) killed plague-carrying rats during the 1902 Australian outbreak.

DURING THE 1921 OUTBREAK of bubonic plague, 35 cases were reported in Sydney with ten deaths. In Brisbane 59 people were struck down with the disease and 28 eventually died.

BUBONIC PLAGUE IS ALSO KNOWN as "The Black Death". It is believed that the disease caused the deaths of an estimated 25 million people during a pandemic in the 14th century.

The single most important group of disease-carrying animals are the insects. Bloodsucking lice (order: Phthiraptera), bugs (order: Hemiptera), fleas (order: Siphonaptera) and flies (order: Diptera), can all transmit viral, bacterial and parasitic diseases. Some of the world's deadliest diseases are spread by insects, including bubonic plague (fleas), epidemic typhus (lice) and malaria (mosquitoes).

IN MOST CASES the disease pathogen is transmitted when the insect's mouth-parts pierce the victim's skin. In other circumstances, the pathogen passes from the insect carrier and gains entry to the host through scratches or breaks in the skin, or from contaminated food that is eaten.

Fortunately, no Australian sucking bugs cause disease. Overseas, cone-nosed and assassin bugs are known to transmit harmful protozoans, particularly *Trypanosoma* species, which cause a range of serious illnesses.

Other insects, such as cockroaches (order: Blattodea), may also carry pathogens that affect human health, simply because they live in dirty conditions.

Right: Australian native cockroaches are common in gardens but none are domestic pests.

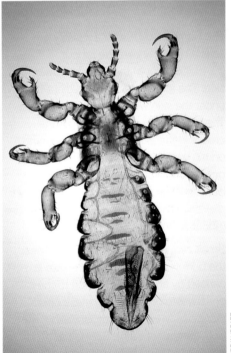

LOUSY LICE

The Human Body Louse (*Pediculus humanus*) is responsible for transmitting epidemic typhus, one of the worst diseases in history. Until the development of a vaccine and antibiotics, epidemic typhus claimed the lives of millions of people around the world. It was once widespread, but now largely occurs in Central America, Asia and Africa. Although body lice occur in Australia, epidemic typhus does not. The bacterium that causes the disease, *Rickettsia prowazekii*, is transmitted when the louse bites. Epidemic typhus is highly contagious and spreads most easily in crowded conditions, such as refugee camps, or where hygiene is poor.

Left: A magnified (20x) picture of the Head Louse (*Pediculus humanus capitus*).

Precautions

Maintain good levels of hygiene and cleanliness. Use insect screens on homes. Treat infested pets and livestock. Ensure outbreaks around the home are attended to promptly.

PESKY FLEAS

Fleas, particularly Oriental Rat Fleas (*Xenopsylla cheopis*), have played a central role in the spread of the ancient scourge of humankind — bubonic plague. The disease is caused by the bacterium *Yersinia pestis* and spread by fleas to rats, especially Black Rats (*Rattus rattus*), and other rodents. Outbreaks of bubonic plague occurred in Australia between 1900–1910 and again in 1921 due to diseased rats escaping from ships.

Scanning Electron Microscope image of a flea.

the FACTS!

AMERICAN COCKROACHES

(below) are one of four introduced pest cockroaches that infest homes and buildings. They generally live in moist areas and are usually found in sewers, crawl spaces, cracks, crevices and foundations. American Cockroaches feed on a wide variety of foodstuffs as well as other plant and animal material.

THE GERMAN COCKROACH is the smallest of the pest species, with adults growing to 1.5 cm in length. It is the most troublesome pest cockroach and the most difficult to eradicate. One female German Cockroach can produce up to 20,000 young annually.

FLIES THAT BITE

Australia has many species of biting fly, including horse or March flies (family: Tabanidae), stable flies (family: Muscidae), black flies (family: Simuliidae) and biting midges or sand flies (family: Ceratopogonidae).

The insects can bite viciously, causing pain and discomfort. With the exception of mosquitoes, Australian biting flies are not known to transmit disease. Reactions to fly bites are usually confined to irritation and sometimes severe allergic responses.

Bushflies (*Musca vetustissima*) breed in cattle dung. The adults are a summertime nuisance when they cluster on humans in large numbers and crawl in the eyes, mouth and nose.

THE HOUSE FLY (*Musca domestica*, below) is a common and familiar pest around dwellings, stables, chicken sheds and rubbish tips. It is found worldwide.

HOUSEHOLD PEST

The German Cockroach (*Blatella germanica*), the American Cockroach (*Periplaneta americana*), the Smoky-brown Cockroach (*P. fuliginosa*) and the Australian Cockroach (*P. australasiae*) are common household pests throughout Australia. All species are introduced.

These cockroaches live in drains, sewers, rubbish tips, grease traps, ceilings and damp cellars as well as under floors. They enter houses and contaminate food with excrement, regurgitated salivary fluid and potentially harmful bacteria.

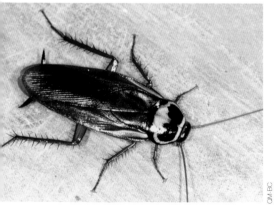

The so-called Australian Cockroach is not native to Australia. They originated in Asia and have become totally adapted to domestic life. These cockroaches can contaminate food and are potential sources of disease in homes and restaurants.

Mammals
— cats, rats & bats

the FACTS!

ONE OF THE DEADLIEST DISEASES that can be passed from animals to humans is anthrax, caused by *Bacillus anthracis*. Almost all cases of human anthrax can be directly linked to contact with infected animals, particularly cattle, or contaminated soil. People most at risk are those who work with the carcases of animals that have died suddenly — meatworkers, farmers, tanners and veterinarians. "Human anthrax" is usually confined to the skin, but if the infection reaches the lungs or digestive tract the disease may prove fatal.

CAVES THAT HAVE BEEN LONG OCCUPIED by bats have deep accumulations of droppings. A number of infectious organisms thrive in these conditions, including the microscopic fungi *Histoplasma capsulatum*. If the spores of this fungus are inhaled, they can cause an acute lung infection.

IN 2001 scientists unlocked the genetic map of the bacterium that causes bubonic plague, *Yersinia pestis*. It was originally a harmless bacterium found in the stomach of rats. About 1500 years ago, it mutated by inserting genes from other bacteria and viruses into its genetic make-up and then entered the bloodstream of its host.

Mammals are probably the animals with which humans have closest contact. Most pets and livestock are mammals and many wild mammals are content to live near people, so it should come as no surprise to find there is a risk of disease.

VIRUSES, BACTERIA AND PARASITES can be transmitted to humans in a number of ways — through bites, contact with animal waste or infected animals, by inhaling dried urine or droppings or by ingesting contaminated food or water.

BITES & SCRATCHES

Bacterial infection from animal bites, especially from cats and dogs, is the most common animal-transmitted disease in Australia. The mouths (and claws) of dogs, cats, rats and other mammals — including humans — harbour huge numbers of bacteria and viruses. Any bite will push these organisms deep into the skin, causing pain and eventually infection. These diseases are often known as "cat scratch fever" and "rat bite fever".

Other animal diseases include Q-fever (spread by livestock and some native animals), yersiniosis (spread by dogs, cats and pigs) and toxoplasmosis (mainly spread by cats).

Right: Feral cats have a home range of 2–6 km² and will eat whatever is available.

THE TROUBLE WITH RATS & MICE

Rats and mice are notorious sources of disease, especially feral species such as the Black Rat (*Rattus rattus*), which have travelled around the globe with humans.

Among these rat-borne diseases is leptospirosis, which is a bacterial disease spread by the inhalation of organisms found in urine of infected rodents. Before the use of mechanical sugar cane harvesting machines, the disease was widespread among cane-cutters because of the large numbers of rats and mice that infested sugar cane plantations.

Although rodents are important carriers of leptospirosis, anyone who works with livestock or wildlife is also at risk. A vaccine given to dairy cattle protects both cattle and farm workers.

The combination of rodents, Oriental Rat Fleas (*Xenopsylla cheopis*) and the bacterium *Yersina pestis* can lead to outbreaks of bubonic plague (*see page 70*).

The Brown Rat (*Rattus norvegicus*) is another rodent that has been dispersed across the globe by humans. Although Brown Rats can harbour diseases, they tend not to live as close to humans as Black Rats.

Precautions

Good personal hygiene is critical, especially thorough hand washing after handling pets, livestock and wild animals. Control rats and mice around homes and workplaces. Treat dogs and cats with worming tablets. Do not kiss domestic pets or livestock. Have sick animals treated by a veterinarian.

BATS — LOW RISK

Many people consider bats, particularly flying-foxes, to be noisy, disease-carrying pests that have no place near humans. However, bats are important pollinators of native plants, particularly hardwood forests, and the risk of disease is small.

Australian Bat lyssavirus was first diagnosed in 1996 in a Black Flying-fox (*Pteropus alecto*) from New South Wales. It has since been detected in other bats. Lyssavirus is similar to rabies, a potentially fatal illness that occurs in many other countries.

Less than 1% of bats carry the virus, which is spread through bites and scratches, not droppings and urine. Most people do not come into contact with bats and their risk of contracting the disease is very low.

Many people have become very fearful of flying-foxes and microbats since the discovery of lyssavirus in Australian bats. However, viral infection from them is easily avoided — do not handle live or dead bats.

PETS — HIGH RISK

The benefits of owning a cat or a dog — especially for children — are indisputable, but our closest animal companions are often overlooked as a source of serious disease. Domestic pets carry a range of parasites including, roundworms, hookworms and tapeworms.

Hydatid disease is caused by small tapeworms, *Echinococcus granulosus*, which live in the intestines of Dingoes, dogs and foxes. Worm eggs pass out of the dogs via droppings and are then picked up by a new host (such as sheep and kangaroos). The worms hatch inside the intermediate host, forming mainly in the liver and lung. If a dog eats these organs, the worm's life cycle is complete. Humans contract the disease when they unknowingly ingest the eggs and the worms form large cysts in various organs.

Children have a high risk of contracting hydatid disease because of their close contact with domestic pets.

the FACTS!

ONLY AUSTRALIA, Japan, New Zealand, Great Britain and a number of island nations are considered to be free of the virus that causes rabies. Dogs are considered to be the main carriers of rabies, but it has also been found in foxes (below), wolves, mongooses, skunks and vampire bats.

INDIGENOUS PEOPLES, who live close to the natural environment, often describe certain places and animals as "unclean" and may have taboos preventing contact. This is a way to describe disease-carrying animals and prevent the spread of disease.

BATS HAVE BEEN IDENTIFIED as carriers of an increasing number of viruses that can infect humans and other animals, including Hendra virus, Nipah virus, Menangle virus, Ebola virus and SARS (severe acute respiratory syndrome) coronavirus. Menangle virus is a rare virus that affects newborn pigs. It was first reported at a large piggery near Sydney in 1997. Hendra virus causes a fatal respiratory disease in horses and it can be transmitted to humans during close contact. Two people have died of Hendra virus. Nipah virus, Ebola virus and SARS have not been reported in Australia.

Environment
— dangers around us

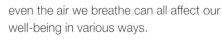

Animals are an essential part of the natural environment. Without them, life on Earth as we know it would probably cease to exist. It is important to understand that even though some animals are "deadly and dangerous", the risks to humans are relatively small. For most of us, a sensible attitude and simple precautions will ensure the safety of ourselves and the animals.

the FACTS!

SUNLIGHT IS CRITICAL to the development and good health of almost every living organism, but over-exposure to the sun's life-giving rays can also cause deadly skin cancer.

EXTREME WEATHER can bring people into closer contact with dangerous animals. Drought and fire may force animals to seek shelter around homes. Cyclones and severe tropical storms may wash dangerous and deadly marine animals inshore and also break up sedentary creatures like cnidarians, leaving stinging fragments floating in otherwise "safe" waters.

IN OUR MODERN WORLD, many other things pose a far greater risk. Water, weather, the sun, dust, plants, chemicals, motor cars, our homes and workplaces, even the air we breathe can all affect our well-being in various ways.

WATER

Some of Australia's most dangerous animals — crocodiles, poisonous fish and box jellies — live in aquatic environments. These "larger" animals can be seen with the naked eye, but watery habitats also hold unseen dangers that are more difficult to detect. Water that looks pure and fresh may have high levels of dangerous pollutants such as chemicals, or may carry microbes and other pathogens that can only be detected through scientific testing.

AIR

Depending on where we live, air pollution can be a major health hazard. Sometimes, the pollution is obvious in the smoky haze that hangs over our cities, but often it remains invisible. Deadly carbon monoxide gas produced in car exhaust fumes is colourless, odourless and tasteless, but it has the power to kill many living things.

Similarly, about one in five people suffer allergic reactions caused by pollen, dust and other microscopic substances in the air. Often we can't see these tiny particles, but we know when they are around because of the runny noses, itchy eyes and breathing difficulties we experience.

Right: Air pollution and carbon dioxide emissions from industrial sources contribute to climate change and human health problems.

Australia's commercial fisheries are highly valued as a source of clean seafood.

WEATHER

Droughts, fires and storms can have major impacts on people and the environment. They can destroy our crops, disrupt our daily lives and cause injury and death. In human terms, the cost of these natural phenomena in suffering, health care, reconstruction and local economies is enormous. They can be equally devastating for animals — through reduced populations, interrupted breeding cycles and the loss of critical habitat areas. Each of these factors can push an endangered species into extinction.

Right: Unexpected weather changes are a trap for travellers. They can easily find themselves stranded by storms and sudden downpours that cause rivers to rise and cut roads.

the FACTS!

CLIMATE CHANGE has the potential to threaten not only humans but also other animals. Fears are held for many species that are restricted to mountain-top environments. If the world climate warms then the conditions that are presently favourable to them will disappear, causing their extinction.

HUMANS ARE NOT THE ONLY ONES AT RISK OF SPREADING DISEASES. The Southern Day Frog (*Taudactylus diurnus*, below) from South-East Queensland became extinct sometime around 1976. The extinction of this and three other frog species from eastern Queensland is mainly due to a highly contagious, virulent, pathogenic fungus *Batrachochytrium dendrobatidis*. This same fungus is also implicated in the extinction of frogs elsewhere in the world.

GLOBAL WARMING is blamed for the melting of polar ice caps and glaciers worldwide. The water released from these is likely to cause a rise in sea levels, threatening coastal communities and islands.

GLOBAL WARMING

Large scale environmental change is altering the nature of our planet. Increasing levels of atmospheric carbon dioxide, generated by human activities, are contributing to the worldwide rise in temperature (global warming). Tied to this is a growing human population that exerts continuing pressure on the Earth's remaining natural areas. The inevitable outcome is that encounters between humans and "deadly and dangerous" animals will increase.

As the planet warms, some animals are moving beyond their normal boundaries. For example, disease-carrying mosquitoes that were previously confined to the tropics are now able to survive in temperate areas.

When the environment becomes unbalanced in this way, it favours the spread of pest species (such as toads and rats) that do not have any special requirements in order to survive successfully. This happens at the expense of native animals and increases the health risk to humans.

As a result of climate change, some regions of Australia may experience unpredictable, sometimes violent, changes of weather.

Further reading

MUSEUMS

www.qm.qld.gov.au/

www.austmus.gov.au/

www.museum.wa.gov.au/

www.samuseum.sa.gov.au/

http://museumvictoria.com.au/

www.tmag.tas.gov.au/

www.artsandmuseums.nt.gov.au/
museums/

GOVERNMENT & OTHER AGENCIES

www.environment.gov.au/about/library/
govtdepts.html

www.gbrmpa.gov.au/

www.aims.gov.au/

www.avru.org/

INJURY/DISEASE RESEARCH & INFORMATION

www.nisu.flinders.edu.au/pubs/bulletin24/
bulletin24-Introduc.html

www.mja.com.au/public/issues/
186_01_010107/mac10709_fm.html

www.marine-medic.com.au/pages/
articles/pdf/parisArticle.pdf

http://www.healthinsite.gov.au/topics/
Infectious_Diseases

http://www.daff.gov.au/animal-plant-
health/pests-diseases-weeds/animal

MARINE ANIMALS

www.fishbase.org/Nomenclature/
NominalSpeciesList.cfm?family
=Tetraodontidae

www.barrierreefaustralia.com/the-great-
barrier-reef/reef_dangers.htm

www.elasmodiver.com/elasmodiver_
home.htm

http://scuba.about.com/od/sharks/
a/sharksattack.htm

http://mpatkin.org/surgery_clinical/
bullraut.htm

www.aims.gov.au/docs/projectnet/sea-
wasp.html

www.taronga.org.au/animals-
conservation/conservation-science/
australian-shark-attack-file/australian-
shark-attack-file

MICROORGANISMS

www.textbookofbacteriology.net/

www.microorganisms.com/

http://library.thinkquest.org/26644/
us/

ARACHNIDS

www.xs4all.nl/~ednieuw/australian/
Spidaus.html

www.findaspider.org.au/

www.spiders.com.au/

www.australiangeographic.com.au/
journal/australian-spiders-the-10-most-
dangerous.htm

www.thedailylink.com/thespiralburrow/

www.anaesthesia.med.usyd.edu.au/
resources/venom/spiders.html

INSECTS

www.csiro.au/places/ANIC

www.mja.com.au/public/issues/
173_04_210800/mcgain/mcgain.html

http://medent.usyd.edu.au/fact/malaria.
htm

MOLLUSCS

www.malsocaus.org/

www.reefed.edu.au/home/explorer/
animals/marine_invertebrates/molluscs

www.mesa.edu.au/friends/seashores/
molluscs.html

www.greatbarrierreefs.com.au/biobits/
biobits_molluscs.htm

AMPHIBIANS

www.frogs.org.au/

www.frogwatch.org.au/

www.corroboreefrog.com.au/corroboree-
frog

www.jcu.edu.au/school/phtm/PHTM/
staff/rsbufo.htm

www.ehp.qld.gov.au/wildlife/threats/
cane_toad.html

REPTILES

www.australiangeographic.com.au/
journal/10-most-dangerous-snakes-in-
australia.htm

www.reptilepark.com.au/our-animals/
reptiles/australian-venomous-snakes/

www.avru.org/general/general_
mostvenom.html

www.environment.gov.au/cgi-bin/sprat/
public/publicspecies.pl?taxon_id=1774

www.nttc.com.au/saltwater-crocodile

www.divethereef.com/guides/
AboutCrocs.asp

Glossary

ADAPT To change physical features over time in order to fit into a particular environment.

AMBUSH A sudden and surprise attack.

ANTIVENOM A serum used to treat a person who has been attacked by a venomous animal.

ARACHNID Eight-legged invertebrate (such as spiders, scorpions and their relatives).

BACTERIA Single-celled micro-organisms found in every habitat on Earth.

BARBELS Slender, fleshy feelers around the mouths of some types of fish (e.g. catfish).

CAMOUFLAGE Colouring that helps an animal blend in with its backgound.

CARAPACE A hard shell that covers the top and sides of an animal's body.

CARNIVORE An animal that eats meat and other animals.

CEPHALOPODS A class of molluscs that includes squids, octopuses and their relatives.

CHELIPEDS Claws/pincers.

CIGUATOXIN A marine poison found in dangerous levels in some large reef fish.

CNIDARIAN Any marine creature of the phylum Cnidaria (corals, hydroids, sea anemones, sea jellies and their relatives).

COLUBRID Any snake that belongs to the Colubridae family. Unlike elapids, Colubrids either lack fangs or have them at the rear of the mouth.

CRUSTACEAN Crabs, crayfish, prawns and their relatives.

DINOFLAGELLATE Microscopic, single-celled aquatic organisms.

ECHINODERM Any slow-moving marine creature that belongs to the phylum Echinodermata (sea stars, sea urchins and their relatives).

ELAPID A snake with hollow fangs positioned at the front of the upper jaw and used for injecting venom.

EXTINCT When an animal, plant, or other living organism ceases to exist.

FERAL A domestic animal (e.g. cat) that has become wild.

GENUS A type, or kind, of animal or plant. The first Latin name of an animal's or plant's scientific name is the genus. Different species can share the same genus.

HERBIVORE An animal that eats plants.

HOST The organism that supports a parasite.

INVERTEBRATE An animal that does not have a backbone.

LARVA (Plural: Larvae) The young form of an animal after it hatches and before it changes into an adult.

MEDUSA (Plural: Medusae) A free-swimming cnidarian (such as a sea jelly). One of two main cnidarian body types.

MOLLUSC An invertebrate animal with a soft body and (usually) a shell.

NEMATOCYSTS Stinging cells.

PARASITE An animal or plant that lives on or in another species (the host) and takes nourishment from them.

PATHOGEN Disease-causing agent.

PEDICELLARIAE Tiny pincer-like structures commonly found on echinoderms.

POLLUTANTS Domestic, agricultural and industrial chemicals that pass into the environment.

POLYP Attaching invertebrates that have a single body cavity. A polyp is one of two basic cnidarian body types.

PREDATOR An animal that hunts and eats other animals.

PROBOSCIS A long, tubular snout or feeding organ.

PROTOZOA Single-celled organisms that can cause serious diseases (such as malaria).

RADULA The rasp-like tongue of most molluscs.

ROSTRUM Part of animal's body that extends out (e.g. a beak).

SPECIES A group of animals that share the same physical features and can breed together to produce fertile young.

SPICULE A small, slender, sharp-pointed body part.

SYMBIOTIC A mutually beneficial relationship between two different species.

TOXIN A poisonous substance produced by living creatures.

VENOM Toxins made by animals that can be injected into prey (via stings, spines, sprays and fangs).

VIRUS A sub-microscopic "agent" that replicates by invading the cells of living organisms.

VULNERABLE A species that has declined and could be at risk of extinction.

ZOOXANTHELLAE Tiny algae that give coral its colour.

Index